MAHABHARATA

THE EPIC

(FOR CHILDREN)

Authors
Kumar Jaimini Shastri
Smt. U. J. Shastri

English Adaptation
Asmita Bhatt

Illustrations
Prakash Bandekar

F 531 E 490

Price : Rs. 250.00

CONTENTS

A MESSAGE FOR CHILDREN

Dear children, before you start reading the Mahabharata, let us quickly acquaint you with the important characters of this epic. Let us tell you about their good and bad qualities.

Yudhishthira was known for his love for truth and justice. He believed in following the principles of *dharma*. Arjuna was admired for his intense concentration, while Bheema was famous for his might and bravery. Karna's generosity and Ekalavya's reverence for a *guru* were unmatched. None could equal the valiant and adventurous Abhimanyu. Kunti's love and affection and her power of endurance, and Draupadi's self-respect and dignity and her faith in Shri Krishna were unique. Vidura was respected for his humble nature and his love for truth, while Bhishma was revered for his solemn vow. The unity of the Pandavas was matchless. Shri Krishna's preaching is relevant even in this age.

Can we adopt at least some of these supreme qualities in our life?

Negative qualities like jealousy, obstinacy and immorality of Duryodhana; cheating, dirty politics and evil designs of Shakuni; Dhritarashtra's blind love for his son; Draupadi's arrogance and harsh, bitter words and Bheema's anger teach us to control our emotions.

The characters of the Mahabharata are created by Maharshi Ved Vyasa. It would be interesting to understand the circumstances, which forced these characters to take the decisions that they took. It would be equally interesting to analyze the consequences of those decisions.

Bhishma should not have made the solemn vow. He should not have sided with the wicked. Draupadi should not have called Duryodhana "The blind son of a blind father." Yudhishthira should not have agreed to play the game of dice. Dusshasana should not have tried to disrobe Draupadi. Duryodhana should not have gestured to Draupadi to sit on his thigh. Duryodhana should not have rejected Shri Krishna's proposal for peaceful settlement.

If you ponder over all these points, you will realize that there is a hidden message in them. Each of them spells out the significance of deep, clear thinking and right actions. When you read about the war of Mahabharata, you feel that the war could have been averted. There should never be any wars.

Shri Krishna was an incarnation of *Narayana*. He always sided with *dharma*. Whenever there is a dearth of righteousness in the world and there is a danger of lawlessness becoming prevalent in the world, he incarnates himself. God always guides and leads the righteous and the virtuous. The one whose life is guided and guarded by God himself has nothing to fear and nothing to worry about. If we do good deeds, there is no reason why Shri Krishna will not be our guide in life.

As you read the Mahabharata, you will understand the subtle message of each incident in it. May the teachings of the Mahabharata be the guiding light in your life.

– Authors

1. SHANTANU

Thousands of years ago, King Shantanu ruled over the kingdom of Hastinapur. One day, Shantanu went on a hunting trip. Searching for a game, he reached the banks of the river Ganga. As he stood there, he spotted a beautiful maiden. Captivated by her beauty, he said, "O beautiful lady! I am Shantanu, the King of Hastinapur. May I know who you are? I wish to make you my Queen and I am prepared to give you all my wealth and riches. Will you marry me?"

The beautiful maiden smiled gently and said, "O King! I am Ganga. I will marry you, but you will have to agree to my conditions."

Delighted to hear this, Shantanu said, "I am ready to fulfil all your conditions in order to marry you."

Ganga said, "You will never ask me who I am or from where I come. Whether you like it or not, you will never stop me from doing whatever I wish. Besides, you will never get angry with me or make me unhappy. The moment you fail to fulfil even one of my conditions, I will leave you and go away."

Shantanu was so struck by the maiden's beauty that he accepted all the conditions laid down by her. Ganga and Shantanu were married with great pomp and gaiety. Ganga was a very beautiful and loving woman. Shantanu was happy to get a wife like her.

In due course, Ganga gave birth to a son. As soon as the son was born, Ganga took him in her arms and walked out of the palace. Shantanu wanted to know where his Queen was going with their son. So, he quietly followed her. When Ganga reached the banks of the river, she threw the baby into the water. Shantanu, who was hiding himself behind a tree, was horrified to see this cruel act of his Queen. He was furious with Ganga. But he had agreed to all her conditions before they got married and so, he remained silent.

3

Ganga gave birth to seven children and, one by one, she threw them all into the waters of the river Ganga. Now Shantanu hated Ganga for her cruelty. But he had promised not to interfere with whatever she did and so he could not say a word to her. When the eighth baby was born, Ganga, as before, took him in her arms and started walking towards the river. This time, too, Shantanu followed her. As Ganga was about to throw the baby into the water, Shantanu stopped her and thundered,

"O cruel woman! Stop. You have killed seven of our sons by throwing them into the waters of the river. What a wicked woman you are! This time, I will not allow you to kill this son."

Hearing these words of Shantanu, Ganga said, "O King! Do you remember your promise? You had agreed not to stop me from doing whatever I pleased. Today, you have broken your promise. So, I will have to leave you and go away. I am Ganga, the goddess of heaven."

"Oh! So you are Ganga, the goddess of heaven!" exclaimed Shantanu.

"But, why did you come down to the earth in the form of a woman?" he asked.

Ganga replied, "Because of a curse by Sage Vasishtha, I had to come down to the earth in the form of a woman. Sage Vasishtha had cursed the eight gods of heaven—the *Ashta Vasus* to be born as human beings on the earth. The *Ashta Vasus* requested me to be their mother, but they wished to return to heaven as soon as they were born. So, they said to me, 'As soon as we are born, please throw us into your waters, so that we may die and return to heaven.'

That was the reason why I had laid down the condition that you would not interfere and stop me from doing whatever I wished to do. All the seven *Vasus* whom I threw into the waters of the Ganga have reached heaven. The eighth *Vasu*, 'Prabhasa', is born to us as our eighth son. I will take him with me. When he grows up, I will hand him over to you."

5

2. THE TALE OF THE *ASHTA VASUS*

Shantanu urged Ganga to stay back but it was all in vain. Ganga did not agree. She took her son and went to heaven. Shantanu was now left all alone and this made him very sad and dispirited.

The eight gods, who were known as the *Ashta Vasus*, lived in heaven. One day, they had gone with their wives onto a mountain on the earth. As they were walking along, they came to the hermitage of Sage Vasishtha. The sage was not in his hermitage at that time. The wife of one of the *Vasus* saw Nandini, the divine cow of Sage Vasishtha, and said, "Get me this cow. I wish to give her as a gift to my friend who lives on the earth."

The *Vasus* were afraid of Vasishtha's wrath. They requested the youngest *Vasu*, Prabhasa, to get Nandini. Prabhasa was adventurous but he never thought about the consequences of his actions. He went to the hermitage and stole Nandini and her calf. The *Vasus* and their wives returned to heaven along with Nandini and the calf.

When Vasishtha returned to his hermitage, he found Nandini and the calf missing. Worried, he sat in meditation to find out what had happened to them. When, with his mind's eye, he saw the evil deed of the *Vasus*, he flew into a towering rage. He cursed the *Ashta Vasus* to be born as human beings on the earth. The *Ashta Vasus* were frightened on hearing the curse of Vasishtha. They went to his hermitage and pleaded,

"O holy man! We have committed a grave mistake. Please forgive us. We will not be able to live happily on the earth. Please take back your curse."

Vasishtha felt sorry for the *Ashta Vasus* and he said to them, "I cannot take back my curse. You will have to take birth as human beings and go down to the earth. But, all the *Vasus*, except Prabhasa, will return to heaven as soon as they are born. Prabhasa will have to spend his whole life on the earth."

On hearing these words of Vasishtha, Prabhasa began to cry bitterly. Consoling him, Vasishtha said, "I bless you that you will be a great man. The people of the earth will honour and respect you for your courage, knowledge and wisdom."

After seeking the blessings of Vasishtha, the *Ashta Vasus* approached Ganga, the goddess of heaven. They said to her, "O goddess Ganga! Please be our mother and free us from the curse of Vasishtha. Go down to the earth and marry a good man. As soon as we are born to you, throw us into the waters of the river Ganga. In this way, we will die and return to heaven immediately."

Ganga was a kind, loving and understanding goddess. She came down to the earth in the form of a woman. She married King Shantanu of Hastinapur. In due course, she gave birth to the eight *Vasus*, one by one. She threw seven of them into the waters of the river Ganga. Thus they were freed from the curse and they returned to heaven. Prabhasa was the eighth son born to Ganga. Shantanu did not allow Ganga to throw Prabhasa into the river. So, according to the conditions put before Shantanu, Ganga left him and went away to heaven along with their eighth son. Ganga named her son 'Devavrata' and brought him up with a lot of love and care. She trained him like a prince. He was also known as 'Gangeya', the son of Ganga.

3. DEVAVRATA

Ganga left Shantanu and returned to heaven. Shantanu continued to lead a lonely and sorrowful life. He gave up all the pleasures of worldly life and started living like a hermit.

One day, Shantanu was taking a stroll on the banks of the river Ganga. Suddenly, he saw a young and handsome boy who possessed the divine looks of Lord Indra. The young boy was shooting arrows into the river as if he wanted to stop the flow of its waters. As Shantanu stood there looking at the boy with amazement, goddess Ganga appeared before him and said, "This is your son Devavrata. I have taught him the Vedas, the Shastras and all the arts. He is proficient in archery and political science. He is a brave and adventurous young man. Now, you may take him with you."

Saying this, Ganga blessed her son Devavrata and disappeared. Shantanu brought his son to his palace.

Shantanu was pleased to have a brilliant son like Devavrata. He crowned him the *Yuvaraja*, the heir to the throne of Hastinapur.

One day, Shantanu was taking a stroll on the banks of the river Yamuna. Suddenly, he got some sweet fragrance. Shantanu went in the direction from which the fragrance was coming. He saw a beautiful maiden. It was the fragrance of her lovely body that was permeating the atmosphere for miles together. This was because of the blessing of a saint. The maiden's name was 'Satyawati', but people fondly called her 'Yojangandha'.

Shantanu requested Satyawati to marry him. Satyawati said, "I am the daughter of a fisherman. My name is Satyawati. You may meet my father and if he agrees, I will be glad to marry you."

Satyawati's father, Daashraja, was the Chief of the fishermen. He was clever but greedy and selfish. He said to Shantanu, "I will give my daughter in marriage to you only if you promise me that her son will be the heir to the throne of Hastinapur."

But Shantanu had already declared Devavrata as the successor to the throne of Hastinapur. He did not want to do injustice to Devavrata by marrying Satyawati. Dejected, he returned to Hastinapur.

After his meeting with Satyawati, Shantanu became sad and disheartened. Devavrata, with the help of a minister, found out the cause of his father's depression. He always wished to see his father happy and so, he went to meet Satyawati's father. He said to Daashraja, "I am Devavrata, the son of King Shantanu. If you give your daughter's hand in marriage to my father, I promise you that only their son will be the heir to the throne of Hastinapur."

Daashraja said to Devavrata, "I trust that you will keep your promise. But your sons will be brave and adventurous like you. What if they, by virtue of their strength, overthrow my daughter's son and seize the kingdom by force?"

Devavrata stretched his hand and declared,

"I, Devavrata, the son of Shantanu, in the presence of the Sun, the Moon and the gods in heaven, vow that I will never marry as long as I live. I vow to live as a celibate throughout my life."

As soon as Devavrata declared his solemn vow, the gods in heaven showered flowers on him. The words 'Bhishma... Bhishma...' resounded throughout the earth and heaven. 'Bhishma' means a man who performs the most difficult task. Since then, Devavrata came to be known as 'Bhishma', the one who makes and keeps the most difficult vow. Devavrata, along with Satyawati, arrived at Hastinapur. Pleased with Bhishma's vow, Shantanu granted him a boon. He said, "You can hold death at arm's length. You can die when you please."

Shantanu married Satyawati. Satyawati gave birth to two sons : Chitrangad and Vichitravirya. Chitrangad was killed in a battle against a *gandharva* called Chitrangad. Vichitravirya, the only surviving heir, was crowned the King of Hastinapur.

13

4. VICHITRAVIRYA

Chitrangad, who was killed in a battle against a *gandharva,* had no son. Therefore, Vichitravirya ascended the throne of Hastinapur.

When Vichitravirya came of age, Bhishma started searching for a suitable bride for him. He heard that the King of Kashi was holding a *swayamwara* for his three daughters Amba, Ambika and Ambalika. They were beautiful, cultured and intelligent princesses and so, many kings and princes from all over the country and abroad came for the *swayamwara.*

Before the *swayamwara* could take place, Bhishma kidnapped the three princesses and drove fast his chariot towards Hastinapur. However, on his way, he was stopped by King Shalva of Saubal. Shalva and Amba had vowed to marry each other. Therefore, Shalva came to rescue Amba. In a fierce battle between Bhishma and Shalva, Shalva was defeated.

On reaching Hastinapur, Bhishma began preparations for the marriage of Vichitravirya. Amba said to Bhishma, "I have chosen, in my heart, Shalva as my husband and have vowed to marry him. Please allow me to go to him."

Bhishma sent Amba back to Shalva. But, when Shalva refused to accept Amba as his wife, she returned to Hastinapur. Bhishma then requested Vichitravirya to marry Amba. Vichitravirya said to Bhishma, "How can I marry a woman who loves another man?"

Amba said to Bhishma, "Nobody is prepared to marry me. You are the one who are responsible for ruining my life. Now I want you to marry me."

15

Bhishma could not marry Amba because of his vow of celibacy. He, once again, sent her to Shalva. But Shalva refused to accept her. Amba was very angry with Bhishma and hated him for being the sole cause of all her miseries. She sought the help of several warriors to punish Bhishma for his deeds, but none came to her help. They were all frightened of Bhishma. At last, Amba performed penance and pleased God. He gave her a garland made of ever-fresh flowers and said, "The one who wears this garland will be able to fight a battle against Bhishma."

Amba took the garland and met many kings, but not one of them was ready to wear it. Disappointed and defeated, Amba hung the garland on the door of the palace of King Drupada and left for the forest. The sages in the forest advised Amba to seek the help of Parashurama. Amba approached Parashurama and narrated her tragic tale to him. Sympathising with her, Parashurama fought a battle against Bhishma but, was defeated. Dejected,

Amba went to the Himalayas and performed harsh penance to please Lord Shiva. Lord Shiva blessed her and said, "In the next birth, you will slay Bhishma."

Amba was very eager to take her revenge and so she jumped into the fire and ended her life to reach heaven.

Meanwhile, the garland still hung on the door of the palace of King Drupada. So, Amba, in her next birth, was born as Drupada's daughter. When Drupada came to know the truth, he wanted to save himself from Bhishma's wrath and so, he sent his daughter away into the forest.

Drupada's daughter performed very harsh penance in the forest. She was transformed into a man who trained himself in the art of warfare. Later, he came to be known as 'Shikhandi'.

5. THE THREE BROTHERS

Vichitravirya married Ambika and Ambalika and they lived happily together for several years. But, being unhealthy and weak from birth, Vichitravirya died at a very young age. He did not have any child of his own. His death left Satyawati and Bhishma in great anxiety because, without an heir, the Kuru dynasty would come to an end. Satyawati said to Bhishma, "You are the only surviving male of the Kuru dynasty. So, I request you to get married in order to produce an heir to the Kuru dynasty."

Bhishma said, "Mother! You may have forgotten my vow, but how can I forget it? I can renounce the three worlds and the kingdom of heaven, but I cannot break my vow."

Satyawati said, "You are not ready to break your vow. I cannot bear to see the end of the Kuru dynasty. So in order to resolve this problem, let us seek the advice of Vyasa Muni."

Bhishma agreed with Satyawati. So, Satyawati thought of her son, the great sage Vyasa and prayed to him. Vyasa appeared before his mother. Satyawati narrated her dilemma and sought his advice. With his divine powers, Vyasa blessed Ambika, Ambalika and one of Ambika's maids with a son each.

Ambika gave birth to 'Dhritarashtra', who was blind from birth. Ambalika gave birth to 'Pandu' and Ambika's maid gave birth to 'Vidura'.

These three sons were born with the blessings of the great sage Vyasa and so, they were rightly declared the heirs to the Kuru dynasty. Bhishma brought them up as his own children.

Dhritarashtra was the eldest of the three brothers. But because he was blind, Pandu ascended the throne of Hastinapur.

When the three princes grew up, Bhishma said to them, "It is your duty to see to it that you carry on the line of the Kuru dynasty. You are of marriageable age now. The daughters of King Subala of Gandhar and the King of Madra are suitable brides for you and for our family. What is your opinion about this?"

Vidura said, "You are our father, mother and *guru*. We are bound to obey you."

Dhritarashtra and Pandu agreed with Vidura. Therefore, Bhishma began preparations for the marriage of the three Princes.

6. THE MARRIAGE OF THE PRINCES

Bhishma heard from some Brahmins that Gandhari, the daughter of King Subala of Gandhar, had received a boon from Lord Shiva that she would be the mother of a hundred sons. So Bhishma sent a messenger to King Subala and asked for Gandhari's hand in marriage for Dhritarashtra. In spite of knowing that Dhritarashtra was blind, Gandhari willingly married him. After her marriage to Dhritarashtra, Gandhari vowed,

"I do not wish to see the world which my husband cannot see."

In order to keep her vow, Gandhari tied a piece of cloth over her eyes. After the marriage of Dhritarashtra and Gandhari, Gandhari's brother Shakuni went to Hastinapur along with them and lived there for the rest of his life.

Shoorsena, the father of Vasudeva, had a daughter named 'Pritha'. There was no match to her beauty and elegance. Shoorsena's cousin Kuntibhoja had no child of his own. So, Shoorsena gave his daughter away to Kuntibhoja as his heiress and hence, Pritha came to be known as 'Kunti'.

One day, the great sage Durvasa was the guest at the palace of Kuntibhoja. Kunti attended on him and served him with devotion. Pleased with her service, Durvasa blessed her and gave her a divine *mantra*. The *mantra* had the power to invoke any god, who would then appear before her and bless her with a son just like him.

One day, Kunti thought, "Let me test the *mantra* given to me by Durvasa." Thinking thus, Kunti chanted the *mantra* and invoked the Sun-god. When the Sun-god appeared before Kunti, she was dazzled by his brilliant light. Trembling with fear, she said, "Please go back. I do not want a son. I only wanted to test the divine *mantra*."

The Sun-god said to Kunti, "You have used the *mantra*, and so I cannot go back without blessing you with a son."

Saying this, the Sun-god gave Kunti a son who was naturally bedecked with a *kavacha* (armour) and *kundals* (ear-rings). Kunti became an unwed mother. Afraid of criticism, Kunti put the baby in a wooden box and set it afloat in the waters of the river Ganga. Floating down the river, the box reached the hands of Adhiratha, a charioteer of Hastinapur. Adhiratha and his wife Radha had been leading a lonely life as they had no child of their own. Adhiratha gave the baby to Radha. They named him 'Vasusena' and started raising him with a lot of love and care.

Meanwhile, Kuntibhoja arranged a *swayamwara* for Kunti to choose her husband. Kings and princes from all over the country and abroad were invited for the *swayamwara*. Pandu also came for the *swayamwara*. Impressed with his personality, Kunti put the garland around his neck. Pandu returned to Hastinapur with Kunti.

After a few days, Bhishma made up his mind to get Pandu married for a second time. He took a big army and went to the capital city of Madra.

The king gave him a grand welcome and asked him the reason of his visit to Madra. Bhishma said, "I have come here to ask for the hand of your daughter Madri for Pandu."

The King of Madra said, "I will be glad to accept your proposal. But according to our family tradition, you will have to give us bridal money."

Bhishma placed before him his vast treasures of gold and ornaments. Then Pandu was married to Madri.

Pandu spent one month in happiness with his two wives. He then set out with his huge army to conquer other kingdoms.

He defeated many kings. They gave him immense wealth as tribute. The victorious Pandu returned to Hastinapur and placed all that he had won at the feet of Bhishma.

Later, Bhishma got Vidura married to Parashavi, the young and beautiful daughter of King Devaka.

7. THE KAURAVAS AND THE PANDAVAS

With the blessings of Lord Shiva, Gandhari gave birth to a hundred sons and one daughter. Besides, Dhritarashtra had also married a Vaishya woman who gave birth to his son named 'Yuyutsu'. Dhritarashtra and Gandhari's daughter was called Dusshala. The young Dusshala was married to King Jayadratha of Sindhu.

Duryodhana was the eldest son of Dhritarashtra and Gandhari. As soon as Duryodhana was born, he began to bray like an ass. Hearing his cry, the vultures, jackals and crows all over the place began to cry. A violent storm hit the city of Hastinapur and fire broke out in many places in the city.

All these natural disasters were considered to be inauspicious omens which predicted the end of the Kuru dynasty. Vidura was aware of that fact. In order to avert future calamities, he advised Dhritarashtra,

"The wise say that for the sake of the family, one member can be abandoned; for the sake of the village, one family can be abandoned; for the sake of the community, one village can be abandoned; and for the sake of saving a soul, everything in the world can be abandoned. Your son is born on this earth to spell its ruin. Therefore, I advise you to abandon him."

Duryodhana being the first born, Dhritarashtra loved him very much and so, he did not heed Vidura's advice which was given with the best of intentions. He began to raise his hundred sons and one daughter with great love and care. The hundred sons of Dhritarashtra came to be known as the 'Kauravas'.

One day, Pandu went on a hunting trip. Suddenly, he spotted a doe and a stag wandering in the forest. Pandu aimed and shot five arrows at them. Wounded and bleeding profusely, the doe and the stag fell down on the ground. When Pandu went near them, he saw a man and a woman lying there wounded by his arrows. Unfortunately, they were actually a sage named Dama and his wife who had assumed the forms of a doe and a stag. Unknowingly, Pandu had wounded them fatally.

Before breathing his last, the sage cursed Pandu,

"You have killed me and my wife. I curse you that you will die when you touch your wife."

Hearing these words of the sage, Pandu was so worried and anxious that he fell ill. His illness made him physically and mentally weak. Tired of life, Pandu went to live in the forest along with his wives Kunti and Madri.

One day, Kunti told Pandu about the divine *mantra* given to her by Durvasa. Pandu gave her his consent to beget children with the help of the divine *mantra*. Thus, Kunti got three sons: Yudhishthira, Bheema and Arjuna. She then gave the divine *mantra* to Madri, who got two sons: Nakula and Sahadeva.

The sons of Pandu came to be known as the 'Pandavas'. The eldest son, Yudhishthira, was born by invoking Dharmaraja. 'Yudhishthira' means the one who remains firm in a battle. The second son, Bheema, was born by invoking Vaayu, the Wind-god. He was born with tremendous strength and energy. His body was strong and heavy. While the Wind-god Vaayu was giving baby Bheema to Kunti, the baby slipped from his hands and fell on a stone on the ground. Baby Bheema was safe, but the stone broke into pieces! Because of his insatiable appetite, he was also called 'Vrukodara', the one with a stomach like a wolf.

The third son, Arjuna, was born by invoking Lord Indra, the King of gods. He grew up to become an ace archer. He was also called 'Parth', the son of Pritha. Arjuna could shoot arrows with both hands and so, he came to be known as 'Savyasachi'. Lord Krishna fondly called him 'Kaunteya', the son of Kunti.

Madri's sons Nakula and Sahadeva were born by invoking Ashvinikumars, the twin-gods. The Ashvinikumars were experts in the medical science. They were the most handsome of all the gods. Nakula and Sahadeva were as good-looking as the Ashvinikumars. Nakula became proficient in horse-riding and Sahadeva was an expert in astrology, but he never predicted anything unless he was asked to!

8. KUNTI AND THE PANDAVAS ARRIVE IN HASTINAPUR

Pandu, along with his wives Kunti and Madri, started living in the forest. He spent the rest of his life meditating, performing harsh penance, fasting and chanting the name of the Lord.

Early one morning, Pandu was taking a stroll in the forest along with Madri. The beauty of the spring had spread all over the forest. The trees and creepers were covered with tender green leaves. Colourful flowers swayed in the gentle breeze. The clear waters of the lakes and ponds reflected the azure of the sky. Fascinated and enchanted by the beauty of the spring, Pandu forgot the curse of Sage Dama. The sage had warned him that he should never touch his wife. But while taking the stroll, Pandu unknowingly held Madri's hand in his. Thus, the curse of the sage came to be true and Pandu died instantly. Madri entrusted her two sons Nakula and Sahadeva to Kunti and immolated herself on the funeral pyre of Pandu.

After Pandu's death, all the sages living in the forest assembled. They decided to take Kunti and the Pandavas to Hastinapur. When they reached the city, they were welcomed with great reverence by Bhishma, Dhritarashtra, Vidura and Satyawati. The sages said to Bhishma, "Pandu lived with us on the Shatashringa mountains and led an austere life. During his stay with us, he became the father of five sons. Kunti gave birth to three sons and Madri gave birth to two. These five children have mastered the Vedas. Pandu died a fortnight ago and Madri immolated herself on his funeral pyre. We have come here with Kunti and the five children. We expect you to welcome them with due honour and give them their rightful place."

Saying this, the sages entrusted the children to Bhishma and returned to the forest.

Bhishma, Dhritarashtra and Vidura were shocked to hear the news of Pandu's death. The whole city of Hastinapur was plunged into grief. Dhritarashtra declared royal mourning throughout the kingdom and asked Vidura to make arrangements for the funeral rites to be performed on Pandu's death. The great sage Vyasa attended the rites.

After the funeral rites were over, Vyasa said to Satyawati, "The days of happiness in Hastinapur have come to an end forever. Grave calamities are knocking at the door of Hastinapur. Henceforth, day by day, there will be an increase in sins. Therefore, I request you to go into the forest and spend the rest of your life singing the glory of the Lord. This will spare you from witnessing the terrible end of your own dynasty."

Satyawati took Bhishma's permission and, accompanied by her daughters-in-law Ambika and Ambalika, went into the forest. They performed harsh penance and in due course, left their bodies and attained heaven.

33

9. DURYODHANA'S JEALOUSY

The Kauravas and the Pandavas were brought up under the supervision of Bhishma. The Pandavas proved themselves superior to the Kauravas in sports. Bheema would easily defeat Duryodhana and his brothers. Many a time, he would pull their hair, tie them up and hang them upside down from a branch of a tree and sometimes, tug at their legs and drag them along the ground. Often, Bheema would grab the Kauravas bathing in the river and pin them down in water. They could barely manage to save themselves and escape. When the Kauravas climbed up a tree to collect fruits, Bheema would vigorously shake the tree so that the Kauravas fell off the tree like ripe fruits. Almost all the Kauravas had some sign of injury caused by Bheema's strength on their bodies. Thus, they always hated Bheema.

The Pandavas and the Kauravas spent their childhood together. Soon the years passed and they grew up to be adventurous young men. This worried Duryodhana a lot. Since Dhritarashtra was blind, Pandu was crowned the King of Hastinapur. Now, after Pandu's death, his eldest son Yudhishthira was crowned the heir to the throne of Hastinapur. Thus, it was certain that he would be the future King of Hastinapur. Dhritarashtra was helpless because of his blindness and so, Duryodhana started hatching plots to prevent Yudhishthira from ascending the throne. But he also knew that as long as the mighty Bheema was with Yudhishthira, no harm would come to him. No one could match Bheema's strength. So, Duryodhana made up his mind to play a clever trick on Bheema in order to get rid of him.

One fine day, the Kauravas and the Pandavas went for a picnic to Pramankotitirth on the banks of the river Ganga. After a swim in the river, they had a hearty meal. Tired, they went to sleep on the banks of the river Ganga.

Duryodhana had mixed poison in Bheema's food. After lunch, Bheema fell into a deep slumber. Duryodhana then tied the sleeping Bheema's arms and legs with some thorny creepers and threw him into the river.

Meanwhile, Bheema drifted in the strong current of the river and was carried down to the *Naga* kingdom (the land of snakes). He was bitten by a thousand snakes. Their poison washed away the poison in his body. When Bheema regained consciousness, the snakes called their king Vasuki. One of the snakes was Aryaka, who was Kunti's maternal grandfather. Aryaka recognized Bheema and took him to a pond which was filled with divine nectar. Bheema was asked to drink all the nectar in the pond. As a result, Bheema gained the strength of ten thousand elephants. The snakes arranged for a bed for Bheema and he went to sleep peacefully.

Meanwhile, in the evening, the Kauravas and the Pandavas woke up and returned to Hastinapur. On their way, Yudhishthira inquired about Bheema. Duryodhana said to Yudhishthira, "I think Bheema must have woken up early and returned home."

But Yudhishthira was worried about Bheema. On reaching home, he asked Kunti, "Mother, has Bheema returned home?"

Surprised, Kunti replied, "No, he hasn't. Why didn't you keep him with you? Why was he left all alone?"

Yudhishthira became pale with worry. Kunti, too, became anxious. She suspected that Duryodhana might have killed Bheema. She rushed to Vidura and informed him that Bheema was missing. Consoling her, Vidura said, "Sister, all the sages have predicted that the Pandavas will live a long life. So, do not worry. I am sure that Bheema will return safely."

Kunti and her sons anxiously waited for Bheema to return home safely.

Bheema slept for eight days in the *Naga* kingdom. When he woke up, he could feel immense strength in his body. The snakes cheered him heartily. Bheema took his leave of them and returned home. He narrated the whole incident to Yudhishthira.

Yudhishthira advised him to keep the incident a secret and also warned him to be careful of Duryodhana.

After a few days, Duryodhana, once again, mixed some poison in Bheema's food. Duryodhana's brother Yuyutsu, who loved the Pandavas, cautioned Bheema and saved his life. After that incident, Duryodhana and his maternal uncle Shakuni tried many methods to kill Bheema, but it was all in vain. However, on the advice of Vidura and Yudhishthira, the Pandavas never revealed to others anything about those events.

10. DRONACHARYA ARRIVES IN HASTINAPUR

Dronacharya was the son of the great sage Bharadwaja. King Prishata of Panchal was a close friend of Bharadwaja. Prishata's son Drupada often visited the hermitage of Bharadwaja. Soon, Drupada and Drona became the best of friends. After the death of Prishata, Drupada was crowned the King of Panchal. Bharadwaja, too, died during that period. Drona spent most of his time in studies and penance. In due course, Drona married Kripi, the daughter of the great sage Sharadwana and the sister of Kripacharya. Kripi was simple by nature. Drona and Kripi had a son named Ashwatthama. Once, the great sage Parashurama was giving away all his wealth, when Drona approached him and asked him for his divine knowledge of weapons.

Drona was so poor that his son Ashwatthama never got a drop of milk to drink. One day, when Ashwatthama saw some children drinking milk, he asked Drona for milk. Drona went to many houses to get a cow, but he returned empty-handed. At last, he mixed some rice flour in water and gave it to Ashwatthama to drink. Thinking that the mixture was milk, Ashwatthama gladly drank it. That day, Drona resolved to seek the help of King Drupada.

Drona went to the court of Drupada and reminded him of their childhood days. But, Drupada was intoxicated with the pride of his wealth and power. He said to Drona, "How can there ever be friendship between a great king like me and a poor Brahmin like you? There can never be any friendship between the rich and the poor, the learned and the ignorant and the brave and the cowardly."

Drona was furious at the haughty behaviour of Drupada. Enraged, he left the court. Drona then went to Hastinapur and began to live with his brother-in-law Kripacharya.

11. THE PRINCES' TRAINING

Kripacharya trained the princes of Hastinapur in archery and the use of arms. Yet, Bhishma was in search of a teacher who could teach them most advanced skills in archery.

One day, a ball with which the princes were playing fell into a well. When Yudhishthira peeped into the well, his ring also fell into it. The princes could not think of any way to retrieve the ball and the ring. Just then, an intelligent looking Brahmin arrived there. The princes told him about their problem and requested him to help them. The Brahmin said to the princes, "You claim yourselves to be Kshatriyas and yet, you are not able to recover the ball from the well. Isn't this shameful? Come, I will retrieve your ball for you."

After chanting some *mantras*, the Brahmin threw a blade of grass into the well. Like an arrow, the blade pierced the ball. The Brahmin then threw another blade, which got stuck to the first one. In this way, the Brahmin threw many blades of grass, one after another, and made a long chain. When the uppermost end of the chain reached the edge of the well, the Brahmin pulled that end and took out the ball from the well. Seeing this miracle, the princes stood there speechless and in utter disbelief. The Brahmin then retrieved Yudhishthira's ring with his bow and arrow.

The princes reported this incident to Bhishma and told him about the Brahmin's miracle. Hearing the princes, Bhishma was sure that the Brahmin could be none other than the famous Dronacharya. Bhishma called Dronacharya and requested him to teach the princes archery and the use of arms. Dronacharya gladly agreed and accepted the responsibility of training the princes.

43

Dronacharya said to the princes, "Henceforth, I am your *guru*. I will teach you the use of arms but, in return, you will have to give me *gurudakshina*. Promise me that you will give me whatever I demand."

Hearing these words, the princes remained silent. But Arjuna came forward and said, "*Gurudev*! I promise you that, as *gurudakshina*, we will give you whatever you ask for."

Seeing Arjuna's reverence for his teacher, Dronacharya warmly embraced him. That day, Dronacharya made up his mind to teach him each and every skill in archery and the use of arms. He resolved to make Arjuna the best archer. Gradually, he made Arjuna the most agile and proficient of all the students.

Every day, the princes had to go to the river to fetch water. Dronacharya had given them pots with very narrow mouths and so, it took the princes very long to fill them with water. Ashwatthama, however, was given a pot with a wide mouth so that he could fill it quickly and return early to the *ashram*. By the time the princes returned, Dronacharya would train his son in the use of arms. When Arjuna came to know about it, he began to fill his pot quickly and return to the *ashram* with Ashwatthama. Therefore, Arjuna got an opportunity to study some extra skills in the use of arms. After a few days, Arjuna tried his hand at shooting arrows in the dark. He succeeded in that, too. When Dronacharya came to know about it, he praised Arjuna and said, "You will be the greatest archer in this world. None will equal your skills in archery."

12. EKALAVYA'S DEVOTION

One day, a young *Bhil* named Ekalavya came to Dronacharya. He paid his respects to Dronacharya and said, "*Gurudev*! I belong to the *Bhil* tribe. My name is Ekalavya and I live in the forest. I wish to learn archery from you. Please accept me as your pupil."

Dronacharya said, "I am here to train only the princes. Therefore, I will not be able to teach you archery."

Disappointed with Dronacharya's reply, Ekalavya returned home. However, he was very keen to learn archery. So, Ekalavya made an earthen idol of Dronacharya and, every day, after bowing to the idol, he would begin his study of archery. In due course, Ekalavya became proficient in archery.

One day, the princes of Hastinapur went on a hunting trip along with their dog. Along the way, the dog strayed and reached the spot where Ekalavya was practising archery and it began to bark continuously. The barking of the dog disturbed Ekalavya's concentration. Irritated, Ekalavya shot many arrows, one after another, into the mouth of the dog. The dog stopped barking. In spite of the innumerable arrows in his mouth, the dog was not injured. The princes, who arrived there, were shocked and amazed to see this. They went to Ekalavya and asked him, "From whom did you learn this wonderful skill in archery?"

Ekalavya replied, "I learnt archery with the blessings of my *guru* Dronacharya."

The princes returned to Hastinapur and informed Dronacharya about the incident. Arjuna said, "*Gurudev*! You had told me that none in this world would equal my skill in archery and that I will be the greatest archer. But, Ekalavya is certainly a greater archer than I am. I feel he has received a greater share of your love and blessings."

Dronacharya said, "Son! I have never taught archery to Ekalavya. His proficiency in archery is the result of his faith, confidence and his reverence for the *guru*. Faith and belief have unmatched strength."

Arjuna took Dronacharya to Ekalavya. Ekalavya bowed to Dronacharya and told him how he had learnt archery. In order to test Ekalavya's devotion for him, Dronacharya said, "You are my pupil and so, you must give me *gurudakshina*."

"Your wish is my command, *gurudev*," said Ekalavya enthusiastically.

Dronacharya said, "As *gurudakshina*, I want you to give me the thumb of your right hand."

Without a moment's hesitation, Ekalavya took a knife, cut off the thumb of his right hand and placed it at the feet of Dronacharya. Arjuna was so impressed with Ekalavya's reverence for his *guru* that he no longer felt jealous of him. Dronacharya was touched by the great sacrifice of Ekalavya. Now, Ekalavya could not even hold the bow with his right hand. Dronacharya said to him, "I am impressed and touched by your unmatched reverence and sacrifice. I bless you that you will be able to practise archery more skilfully with your left hand."

49

13. THE PRINCES DISPLAY THEIR SKILLS

Dronacharya trained the princes in the use of arms. The princes had now finished their training. So, one day, a function was arranged so that the princes could publicly display the skills mastered by them. The people of Hastinapur were also eager to see the skills of their princes.

A pandal was set up on a spacious open ground. Bhishma, Dhritarashtra, Gandhari, Kunti and others came to witness the grand event. The pandal was full of spectators. The beat of drums and sound of trumpets permeated the atmosphere. With the permission of Bhishma, the function began and Vidura started describing the happenings to Dhritarashtra.

Each prince came into the arena and displayed his skills in the use of arms. A single combat between Bheema and Duryodhana left the spectators spellbound. Because of their personal rivalry and hatred, they had actually started fighting with each other! At last, Ashwatthama intervened and separated the two rivals. Finally, the great archer, Arjuna came on the stage. He used the *Aagneyastra* to light the fire and immediately thereafter, he used the *Varunastra* to bring the rain. Arjuna dazzled the spectators by displaying his skills in the use of many other divine weapons. They gave him a standing ovation. This, however, made Duryodhana more jealous of Arjuna.

Suddenly, the tall, strong and well-built Karna came into the arena. In a deep voice he addressed the spectators,

"Just a little while ago, Arjuna displayed his skills on this stage. But I can definitely show better skills than he has displayed."

A delighted Duryodhana said, "O brave Karna! Go ahead and display your skills."

Karna said, "But, before that, I wish to challenge Arjuna to single combat."

Kripacharya interrupted and said, "You are the son of a charioteer, whereas Arjuna is a prince. A son of a charioteer has no right to fight a duel with a prince."

"In that case, I crown Karna the King of Anga." Saying this, Duryodhana performed the coronation ceremony of Karna.

Arjuna arose from his seat and said to Karna, "Karna! You may be a brave man. But do not be under the impression that you are the only one who is thus blessed. So, you must remember that I will never show my back when challenged even by the best and the greatest in the world."

Arjuna's bold and defiant words were loudly cheered and welcomed by the spectators. But by then, Bhishma had announced the function to have ended. The harsh words of Arjuna resounded in Karna's ears and pierced his heart like thorns. At that moment, Karna made up his mind to teach Arjuna a lesson.

14. KARNA

Karna was born as Vasusena. Before Kunti married King Pandu, Surya, the Sun-god, had blessed her with a son. But fearing slander by people, Kunti abandoned him.

A charioteer named Adhiratha and his wife Radha found Vasusena. They brought him up as their own child with a lot of love and care. Vasusena grew up to be a very strong young man. Every morning, he worshipped Surya. He would continue his prayers till the rays of the sun scorched his back. He did not wish to become a charioteer. He wanted to become an ace warrior. He began to learn archery at the age of sixteen. He approached Dronacharya and requested him to teach him archery. But Dronacharya refused to teach him. Vasusena then went to Parashurama to learn archery from him. Parashurama taught only Brahmins. Therefore, Vasusena made a false declaration and introduced himself as a Brahmin. Parashurama trained Vasusena in archery. Vasusena impressed Parashurama with his sharp intelligence and skills. Parashurama also taught him how to use the *Brahmastra*.

One day, Parashurama fell asleep with his head in Vasusena's lap. Suddenly, a wasp stung Vasusena on his thigh. But he did not even move. The wasp stung him even more sharply. The wound started bleeding. Vasusena did not want to disturb his *guru's* peaceful sleep. So, in spite of the unbearable pain, he sat still. As soon as the blood touched Parashurama's head, he woke up. He now knew that a man with such a great power of endurance could not be a Brahmin. Furious, Parashurama began to interrogate Vasusena. Vasusena revealed his true identity and also apologized to his *guru*. But, Parashurama was not pacified. He cursed Vasusena :

"You lied to me in order to learn archery. At the time of an emergency, when you need it most, you will forget how to use the *Brahmastra*."

A dejected Vasusena accepted his mistake and left for home.

One day, Lord Indra came to him in the form of a Brahmin and asked him for his *kavacha* (armour) and *kundals* (ear-rings). Vasusena was a generous man. He recognized the Brahmin to be Lord Indra. Yet he gladly gave away his *kavacha* and *kundals* which had protected him ever since he was born. Since then, he came to be known as 'Karna'. This brave Karna became Duryodhana's best friend. Till his death, Karna remained loyal to Duryodhana.

15. DRONACHARYA'S *GURUDAKSHINA*

One day Dronacharya called all the princes and said, "I have done my duty by teaching you the use of arms. Now you have to give me my *gurudakshina*. King Drupada of Panchal had insulted and humiliated me in his court. I want you to defeat him in a battle, seize him alive and bring him to me."

Following the *guru's* orders, the princes attacked the kingdom of Panchal. Arjuna, with his skills in archery, defeated the army of Panchal and captured Drupada. The princes then produced Drupada before Dronacharya.

With a victorious smile on his face, Dronacharya said to Drupada, "Now that I have conquered your kingdom, I am the king. You are no longer a king and so, you cannot match my status or be my equal. I am giving you half the kingdom. Thus, both of us are now equals. Do you wish to say anything in this matter?"

Drupada stood silent, with his head bent down in embarrassment. He had no choice but to bear the insult quietly. In this way, Dronacharya took his revenge on Drupada by insulting him. Later, however, Dronacharya returned the entire kingdom to Drupada.

Drupada was embarrassed and infuriated by Dronacharya's insults. For a long time he fasted, meditated and performed harsh penance to appease the gods. At last, the gods asked him to seek a boon. Drupada asked the gods to bless him with a son who could kill Dronacharya and a daughter who would marry Arjuna. The gods granted the boon and blessed him with such a son and a daughter as he had wished for. Drupada named his son 'Dhrishtadyumna' and his daughter 'Draupadi'.

16. THE WAX PALACE OF VARANAVATA

Duryodhana hated the Pandavas. But the people of Hastinapur loved the Pandavas and praised them highly. They would say,

"Being blind, Dhritarashtra is not able to look after the administration of the kingdom. Bhishma, because of his vow, will never ascend the throne of Hastinapur. Therefore, Bhishma should crown Yudhishthira the King of Hastinapur."

Hearing this, Duryodhana became more jealous of the Pandavas and hated them so much that he devised a plan to kill them. He went to Dhritarashtra and said, "Father! If Yudhishthira is crowned the King of Hastinapur, what will happen to us and our children? If we become their dependants, our lives will be no better than those of beggars."

Hearing these words of Duryodhana, Dhritarashtra was worried. He said to Duryodhana, "In that case, what can we do? The people love the Pandavas. If we do any injustice to them, the people of Hastinapur will revolt against us."

Duryodhan said, "I want you to send the Pandavas to Varanavata. In their absence, we can gather the support of the people of Hastinapur. Gradually, the people will forget the Pandavas."

According to the advice given by Duryodhana, Dhritarashtra called the Pandavas and said, "A big celebration in honour of Lord Shiva is being held in Varanavata. Many people from far and wide will come for this celebration. The people of Varanavata wish to have you as their guests. Therefore, you should go there not only to participate in the celebration but also to fulfil the wish of the people of Varanavata."

Obeying Dhritarashtra, the Pandavas, along with Kunti, took the blessings of the elders and left for Varanavata. Vidura said to Yudhishthira, "The one who knows beforehand the plot of a clever enemy, can alone escape the danger of death."

"The fire which can reduce the whole forest to ashes, cannot even touch the mouse hiding in its hole under the ground," he added.

Vidura's words signalled a warning about the evil plot of Duryodhana and also hinted at the way in which the Pandavas could escape from the danger. Yudhishthira bowed to Vidura and said, "I understand what you mean. Please do not worry about anything."

On their way to Varanavata, Yudhishthira told his brothers and Kunti about the evil designs of Duryodhana.

Duryodhana had already sent Purochana, his trusted minister, to Varanavata. Purochana had got a palace built for the Pandavas and their mother Kunti. While entering the palace, Yudhishthira observed it minutely. The palace was built with inflammable materials like wax, ghee and cloth made of flax. Yudhishthira said to his brothers, "We have to pretend as if we know nothing. Before this palace is set on fire, as soon as we get the right opportunity, we will get out of it."

At that moment, an artisan came there and said, "Vidura has sent me to help you. You remember his words, don't you?"

This artisan had secretly dug a tunnel which would lead the Pandavas out of the palace safely. Meanwhile, Purochana was looking for an opportunity to set the wax palace on fire. Soon a year passed.

One day, Yudhishthira noticed that Purochana looked impatient and nervous. He immediately warned his brothers to be careful. That day, the Pandavas performed a *yagya* and arranged for a grand feast for the people of Varanavata. Purochana and the servants of the palace relished the feast and went off to sleep. At night, an old woman and her five sons came to the palace and slept in the verandah of the palace.

At midnight, Bheema set Purochana's room on fire. The Pandavas and Kunti then left the wax palace through the secret tunnel. Soon the whole wax palace was ablaze. Purochana, the old woman and her five sons were burnt to death in that fire.

Next morning, the news of the fire in the wax palace spread in Varanavata. When the people saw the badly burnt bodies of the old woman and her sons, they thought that Kunti and her sons had been burnt to death. This news was sent to Hastinapur. The whole kingdom of Hastinapur was plunged into grief but, Duryodhana and Dhritarashtra were very pleased. Vidura knew that the Pandavas and Kunti were alive and safe. He informed Bhishma about it.

After coming out of the wax palace, the Pandavas reached the banks of the river Ganga. A boatman, who was sent by Vidura, was waiting for them. The Pandavas and Kunti sat in the boat and he rowed them safely across the river.

65

17. THE SLAYING OF HIDIMB

On reaching the opposite bank of the river Ganga, the Pandavas entered a thick forest. They walked the whole night, through the prickly thickets and over the rocks. Sometimes, they heard the frightening cries of wild animals. Soon they were exhausted. Kunti was very thirsty. Bheema asked everybody to sit under a tree and went in search of water. Bheema took some water from a nearby lake. When he returned, his mother and brothers were fast asleep. Bheema could not bear to see their plight and his eyes were filled with tears.

A demon named Hidimb lived near that lake. Hidimb said to his sister Hidimba, "I smell man. Go and search the surrounding area. If you see a man, bring him to me. I want to devour his flesh."

Wandering in search of a man, Hidimba came to the tree under which Kunti and her four sons were fast asleep. She spotted Bheema. Seeing his well-built and strong body, she fell in love with him. Hidimba transformed herself into a beautiful maiden and went to Bheema. She said, "My brother Hidimb has sent me here because he wants to kill all of you and eat you up. But on seeing you, I have fallen in love with you. I wish to marry you. Please wake these people up. I will use my magical powers and take you to a safe hiding place."

Bheema said to Hidimba, "My mother and brothers are fast asleep. They are very tired. I do not want to disturb their peaceful sleep now. Please do not worry about us. However strong your brother may be, he cannot harm us. I will handle him."

At that moment, Hidimb arrived there. When he saw Bheema talking to his sister Hidimba in the form of a beautiful woman, he flew into a towering rage. He roared, "I had sent you here to kill these people; but you have fallen in love with this man! You are exhibiting your beauty in front of this lowly creature! Aren't you ashamed of yourself?"

Saying this, Hidimb rushed to kill Hidimba. Bheema intervened and said, "You cruel demon! Control yourself, I dare you to touch this woman in my presence. If you have the courage, I challenge you to fight a duel with me or else I order you to leave this place quietly."

On hearing the challenging words of Bheema, Hidimb rushed towards him. He roared loudly and punched Bheema. But Bheema was unperturbed. There was a fierce duel between Bheema and Hidimb. Hearing the thundering noises of the fight, the birds and animals of the forest began to run helter-skelter. Soon Kunti and the four brothers also woke up. Bheema lifted Hidimb high in his hands and hurled him down violently. Hidimb hit the ground with a thud and died instantly.

18. BHEEMA AND HIDIMBA

Arjuna said to Yudhishthira, "I think we should go far away into the forest, otherwise Duryodhana's men will find us."

Yudhishthira agreed with Arjuna. After drinking some water, they started walking further. Hidimba, too, followed them quietly. After some time, when Kunti turned around, she saw Hidimba. Kunti was surprised to see a fairy-like beautiful maiden following them. Kunti stopped there and asked Hidimba, "Why are you following us? Come here and introduce yourself to me."

Hidimba bowed to Kunti and said, "Mother! I am Hidimba, the sister of Hidimb—the demon. I have fallen in love with your son, the one who killed my brother. Since my brother is dead, I have none to support me now. I beg of you to oblige me by accepting me as your daughter-in-law."

Kunti put Bheema's hand in Hidimba's and said, "If you love each other, who am I to stop you from getting married? You may take Bheema with you. You may have him with you throughout the day but, you must send him to us at night. We need Bheema to protect us at night."

Having said this, Kunti asked Bheema, "Bheema! Do you, too, like this girl?"

Bheema blushed. Kunti blessed Bheema and Hidimba and bid them farewell.

Bheema stayed with Hidimba during the day. At night, however, he would return to his mother and brothers, no matter where he was. Bheema and Hidimba had a son named 'Ghatotkacha'. The Pandavas now wished to leave the forest and settle down in a town. So Bheema took his leave of Hidimba. Ghatotkacha said to Bheema, "Father! Grandmother has asked me to stay with mother. Please do not forget us. Whenever you need me, you must call me to you."

19. THE SLAYING OF BAKASURA

The Pandavas and Kunti proceeded on their journey through the thick forest. One day, they came across Maharshi Vyasa, the great sage. The Pandavas bowed to him. Kunti broke down and narrated to Maharshi Vyasa their tragic story of hardships and suffering. Consoling her, Maharshi Vyasa said, "These days, too, will pass. The wheel of happiness and gloom keeps on moving continuously. Man must always perform his *dharma*. It is man's duty to fulfil his obligation."

The Pandavas were encouraged and energized by the wise words of Vyasa. As advised by him, the Pandavas disguised themselves as Brahmins and went to the town of Ekachakra. They began to live in the house of a Brahmin.

Every morning, the Pandavas went around the town begging for food. Whatever they received would be divided into two equal halves. One half was shared by Yudhishthira, Arjuna, Nakula, Sahadeva and Kunti. The other half was given to Bheema. But, even that did not satisfy Bheema's great appetite.

One day, the Pandavas had gone to beg for food. Bheema had stayed back at home to look after Kunti. Suddenly, Kunti heard the Brahmin and his wife crying. Kunti went to them and asked them the reason why they were crying. The Brahmin said, "A demon named Bakasura lives in the nearby forest. He used to come to our town and eat up many people. Our king could not protect us from the atrocities of Bakasura. Therefore, the people of the town made an arrangement with the demon. We assured him that he would be provided with a cart-load of food and one human being every week. Since then he has stopped harassing us. The people of the town have fixed turns to go to Bakasura with food. Today, it is my turn to go to him with food. This is my last day with my wife and children. This is the reason why we are crying."

Kunti said to the Brahmin, "O Brahmin! We are indebted to you. Therefore, today, instead of you, my son will go to Bakasura with the food. Bakasura will not be able to harm him."

Initially, the Brahmin refused Kunti's proposal. But when Kunti narrated to him Bheema's acts of bravery and adventure, he agreed to send Bheema to Bakasura.

Bheema set out in a bullock-cart filled with food for Bakasura and soon reached the cave where he lived. Being very hungry, Bheema sat there and started eating Bakasura's food. Bakasura, who was eagerly waiting for his food, came out of the cave. When the hungry demon saw Bheema eating his food, he flew into a towering rage. He started kicking and punching Bheema. But Bheema was not at all affected by this attack. After finishing all the food that he had brought, Bheema got up and confronted the demon. A fierce duel ensued between the two. When Bakasura was exhausted, Bheema punched him hard in his chest. Bakasura gave out a loud roar and fell down dead with a heavy thud. Bheema dragged Bakasura's dead body and brought it to Ekachakra. The people of the town rejoiced over the death of the cruel and tyrannical Bakasura.

75

20. ARJUNA WINS DRAUPADI

King Drupada of Panchal held a *swayamwara* for his daughter Krishna. Krishna was also known as 'Draupadi' – the daughter of Drupada. Many Brahmins from Ekachakra were heading for Panchal to participate in the festivities of the *swayamwara* and to receive gifts and alms. Maharshi Vyasa met the Pandavas and advised them to take part in the *swayamwara*. So, the Pandavas, along with the other Brahmins, went to Panchal. On their way, they met a Brahmin, an ascetic, named Dhaumya. Impressed with Dhaumya's intelligence and knowledge, the Pandavas made him their *purohit* – the family priest. On reaching Panchal, the Pandavas took shelter in a potter's house.

The whole town of Panchal was beautifully decorated for the occasion. Music, dance, sports and other entertainment programmes were held at various places. A huge pandal was built for Draupadi's *swayamwara*. Kings, princes and ministers from all over the country and abroad had come to take part in the *swayamwara*. Duryodhana, Dusshasana and Karna had also come from Hastinapur. Shri Krishna and Balarama came from Dwarika.

Melodious music permeated the atmosphere as Draupadi, dressed in her bridal finery, entered the pandal accompanied by her brother Dhrishtadyumna. With her unmatched beauty and elegance, Draupadi looked like a heavenly nymph. She wore beautiful silk clothes. Bedecked with precious ornaments of gold, silver, diamonds and rubies, she looked even more beautiful. Draupadi had a garland of fragrant flowers in her hands.

Dhrishtadyumna stood before the assembly and announced,

"Here is the bow and an arrow. There is the target – a golden fish fixed on a disc on the top of a pillar in the middle of the pond. The disc is revolving rapidly. Draupadi will marry the man who will, by shooting an arrow pierce the eye of the fish above by looking at its reflection in the water below."

One by one, many kings and princes came forward and tried to hit the target. But none succeeded. Everybody present in the assembly was disappointed. At last, Karna came forward to try his luck. There was a murmur of protest in the assembly. When Draupadi heard that Karna was the son of a charioteer, she protested and said, "Even if Karna succeeds in hitting the target and felling it, I will not marry him."

At that moment, Arjuna, who was sitting among the Brahmins, arose and walked towards the bow. He picked up the bow and shot an arrow which hit the target. The kings and princes who had failed earlier, doubted the skill and success of Arjuna. Arjuna, once again, took aim and shot an arrow which hit the target. The fish fell down on the ground. Draupadi gladly put the garland round Arjuna's neck.

The kings who had come to take part in the *swayamwara* felt humiliated and could not bear the fact that a Brahmin, with his skills in archery, was marrying a Kshatriya maiden. They got together and prepared themselves to fight with Arjuna. Bheema left the pandal and uprooted a nearby tree. He put the tree on his shoulders and stood firmly next to Arjuna. Seeing the monstrous appearance of Bheema, the kings were frightened. Shri Krishna pacified them and requested them to leave. He then said to Balarama, "I had heard that aunt Kunti and the Pandavas had safely escaped from the wax palace in Varanavata. I think that the Brahmin, who fell the target, is none other than Arjuna."

Arjuna and Bheema returned to the potter's house along with Draupadi. Dhrishtadyumna quietly followed them. Bheema stood outside the house and said to Kunti in a loud voice, "Mother! Today we have brought a very nice gift for you."

Kunti replied, "Whatever you have brought, share it equally among yourselves."

After a while, when Kunti came out of the house, she saw Draupadi. Kunti was puzzled. Arjuna said to her, "Mother! Your words will be honoured. All five of us will marry Draupadi."

Dhrishtadyumna overheard the conversation between the Pandavas and Kunti. He now realized that the Brahmin, the skilled archer, who had felled the fish, was none other than Arjuna. He returned to the palace and informed his father King Drupada about the Pandavas. King Drupada was overjoyed to hear the news. But when he heard that Draupadi was ready to marry the five brothers, he was worried. Maharshi Vyasa told him that in her last birth, Draupadi was blessed by Lord Shiva. He had granted her a boon to have five husbands. Therefore, what had happened was inevitable. King Drupada sent Dhrishtadyumna and the royal priest to the potter's house to bring Kunti and the Pandavas to the palace.

Drupada performed the marriage of Draupadi with the Pandavas according to the Vedic rites. He gave Draupadi a hundred golden chariots, a hundred elephants and a hundred maids as gifts.

21. THE PANDAVAS' ARRIVAL IN HASTINAPUR

The news of the marriage of the Pandavas with Draupadi spread like wild fire. When Dhritarashtra heard the news, he was not at all pleased. Yet, fearing criticism from the people, he pretended to be happy and exhibited false pleasure. Bhishma and Dronacharya compelled Dhritarashtra to send Vidura to King Drupada of Panchal in order to bring the Pandavas back to Hastinapur.

After Vidura left for Panchal, Duryodhana, Dusshasana, Shakuni and Karna met Dhritarashtra. They began to instigate him against the Pandavas. Karna said to Dhritarashtra, "Dronacharya has earned his living from your wealth; yet why did he give you such an advice as would benefit our enemy?"

Duryodhana, too, agreed with what Karna said. Dhritarashtra was in a dilemma.

When the Pandavas, Kunti and Draupadi arrived in Hastinapur along with Vidura, they were given a grand reception by the people. The whole town was beautifully decorated to welcome the Pandavas. The Pandavas, Shri Krishna, Draupadi and Kunti came into the palace. They bowed to the elders and sought their blessings.

Dhritarashtra handed over half the kingdom of Hastinapur to the Pandavas and crowned Yudhishthira the king. He said to Yudhishthira, "In order to avoid any conflict or hostility in the family, shift the capital of your kingdom to Khandavaprastha and live there. There is a dense forest there now. But in ancient times, our forefathers had their capital there. If you live there, it may end the hatred and ill-will between you and the Kauravas."

Obeying Dhritarashtra, the Pandavas, along with Draupadi and Kunti, arrived in Khandavaprastha. They cleared the forest and built new palaces there. In due course, the forest was transformed into a beautiful town. This town came to be known as 'Indraprastha'. The hard work and prosperity of the Pandavas made Indraprastha famous far and wide. The Pandavas ruled over Indraprastha for thirteen years. The people lived happily during their rule. As a result, their fame spread all over the world.

22. ARJUNA'S EXILE

One day, Narada came to Indraprastha and said to the Pandavas, "Your brotherly love is unmatched. Yet, you should frame a code of conduct regarding living with Draupadi. This will prevent any misunderstanding among you in future."

Thereafter, the Pandavas decided that Draupadi would live with each brother for a year. If any of the other brothers intruded on their privacy during that period, he would have to go into exile for twelve years.

One day, Arjuna needed his weapons to rescue the cows of a poor Brahmin from the clutches of some dacoits. Arjuna's weapons were lying in Yudhishthira's palace. At that time, Draupadi was living with Yudhishthira. In spite of knowing this, Arjuna went to Yudhishthira's palace and got his weapons. Thus, Arjuna had to violate the code of conduct in order to fulfil his duty. Arjuna restored the cows to the Brahmin and went straight to Yudhishthira. He sought his permission to go into exile. Yudhishthira tried to stop Arjuna, but it was all in vain. Arjuna was determined to atone for his violation of the code of conduct.

Arjuna began his journey into exile for twelve years. One day, while Arjuna was bathing in the river Ganga, he was spotted by Ulupi, the daughter of Kairavya, the king of snakes. Ulupi dragged him to *Nagaloka*, the kingdom of snakes. Arjuna married Ulupi and spent a night with her in the *Nagaloka*. Ulupi conferred a boon on Arjuna,

"You will be able to walk in water just as you walk on land and no marine creature can ever harm you."

Having said this, Ulupi brought Arjuna back up to the land. Arjuna proceeded on his journey. In due course, Ulupi gave birth to a son named 'Iravana'.

After a long journey, Arjuna reached Manipur. Princess Chitrangada of Manipur was a beautiful maiden. Arjuna married Chitrangada and lived with her for three years. Chitrangada gave birth to a son named 'Babhruvahana'. Arjuna then left Manipur and continued his journey.

One day, Arjuna saw five lakes in a place. But he was surprised to see that the surrounding area was deserted. Meanwhile, some ascetics came there and said to Arjuna, "This is Saubhadratirth, the region of five lakes. In each of these five lakes there lives a crocodile. Anyone who enters any of the lakes is killed by the crocodile living in it. Therefore, the surrounding area remains deserted."

Arjuna bravely entered one of the five lakes and began to enjoy swimming in the water. Suddenly, a crocodile caught his leg. But Ulupi, the *Naga* maiden, had conferred a boon on him that no water creature could ever harm him. Thus, Arjuna dragged the crocodile to the bank of the lake. As soon as the crocodile came to the bank, it was transformed into a beautiful maiden. She said to Arjuna, "I am an *apsara* from heaven. My name is Varga. My four friends, Saurabheyi, Sameechi, Budbuda, Lata and I were cursed by a Brahmin who turned us into crocodiles. The Brahmin had told us that after a hundred years a great man would release us from the curse. Since you have released me from the curse, you must be that great man. Now, I request you to free my four friends from the curse."

Arjuna released Varga's four friends from the curse of the Brahmin and continued his journey. After a few days, he reached Prabhasa, a place of pilgrimage near Dwarika. When Shri Krishna learned about his arrival, he came to Prabhasatirth. Arjuna and Shri Krishna were the human forms of *Nar* and *Narayana*. Thus they embraced each other lovingly. Shri Krishna then took Arjuna to Dwarika.

One day, the Yadavas held a grand celebration on the Raivataka mountain. Arjuna was their guest of honour. Suddenly, Arjuna spotted a beautiful young maiden amidst the crowd. She was Subhadra, Shri Krishna's sister. Shri Krishna understood Arjuna's feelings. He, therefore, advised Arjuna to elope with Subhadra.

One day, Subhadra went to a temple on the Raivataka mountain. Arjuna waited for her outside the temple in Shri Krishna's chariot. As soon as Subhadra came out after finishing her worship, Arjuna lifted her up, placed her in the chariot and drove away. When Shri Krishna's brother Balarama and the other Yadavas heard the news of Subhadra's abduction, they were furious. Shri Krishna pacified them. At last, Arjuna and Subhadra were called back to Dwarika and were married according to the Vedic rites. Arjuna lived with Subhadra in Dwarika for one year and then spent some time in Pushkar. Soon the twelve years of exile were over. So Arjuna returned to Indraprastha along with Subhadra.

In due course, Subhadra gave birth to Abhimanyu. Draupadi gave birth to Prativindhya, Shrutasena, Shrutakirti, Shataneek and Shrutakarma. Acharya Dhaumya taught them the Vedas and also taught them the use of weapons. The princes became proficient in art of warfare.

With the help of his brothers, Yudhishthira conquered and annexed many kingdoms. The Pandavas ruled according to the principles of *dharma* and the rules of ethics. So their fame and glory spread far and wide.

23. THE BURNING OF THE KHANDAVAVANA

One day, Shri Krishna and Arjuna were taking a stroll on the banks of the river Yamuna. Suddenly, a Brahmin came to them and said, "I am Agnideva, the God of Fire. I wish to consume the Khandavavana. But Lord Indra's friend, Takshaka, the king of serpents, lives in that forest. Therefore, whenever I set the forest on fire, Lord Indra comes to Takshaka's rescue. Lord Indra comes down with a heavy rainfall and extinguishes the fire. I have to escape from there and thus, I always remain hungry. I know both of you possess divine powers. I request you to help me burn the Khandavavana by stopping Lord Indra with the help of your weapons."

Arjuna said to Agnideva, "We are prepared to help you. But you must give us such divine weapons as can be used in the battle against Lord Indra."

Agnideva gave Arjuna a bow called *gandeev* and two quivers which would always remain full of arrows. He also gave him a chariot called *Nandighosh*. Agnideva gave Shri Krishna the *Sudarshanchakra* and a mace called *Kaumudaki*.

The Khandavavana was a dense forest. Hence it had become a hiding place for many dangerous criminals. It was necessary to eliminate them for the peace and happiness of the people of Indraprastha. Arjuna was mighty pleased when Agnideva began the work of getting rid of the criminals. Arjuna and Shri Krishna stood on the path leading out of the forest. As soon as Arjuna gave a signal, Agnideva began his work.

Huge flames engulfed the forest and soon they reached the skies. Innumerable birds, insects and animals were burnt alive in that fire.

When Lord Indra came to know about the fire in the Khandavavana, he immediately rushed there along with the rain clouds. But, Arjuna blew the rain clouds away with the help of the *Vayavyastra*.

The angry Lord Indra chopped off the peak of Mount Mandar and hurled it at Arjuna. Arjuna broke it into pieces with the help of his divine arrows. At that moment there was a message from heaven :

"O Indra! Your friend Takshaka, the king of serpents, has left the Khandavavana and he is safe. Stop worrying about him and let this forest, which is full of dangerous criminals, burn to ashes."

Lord Indra apologized to Shri Krishna and, after giving his blessings to Arjuna, returned to heaven. Meanwhile, a demon named Maya escaped from the clutches of Agnideva. Shri Krishna was ready to kill him. But Maya fell at Arjuna's feet and pleaded with him to save his life. Arjuna gave him a solemn promise and saved his life. Agnideva burnt the Khandavavana for fifteen days. At last, he thanked Shri Krishna and Arjuna and returned to heaven.

Maya said to Arjuna, "You have saved my life. Now, you must give me an opportunity to serve you. I possess exceptional skills in extraordinary architecture."

Arjuna asked Maya to build a palace for the Pandavas. In a short time, Maya constructed a unique palace. The palace was constructed with such extraordinary optical illusions that it was very difficult to differentiate between a pond of water and the crystal floor. The Pandavas were thrilled to see the magnificent palace and they thanked Maya for his efforts.

Maya gave Bheema a golden mace with weight equal to that of a thousand ordinary maces. He also gave Arjuna the *Devadatta*, a conch with an extremely loud sound. At an auspicious time, the Pandavas entered the magnificent palace.

24. THE SLAYING OF JARASANDHA

The Pandavas began to live in the palace constructed by Maya. One day, Narada Muni came to visit them. He advised Yudhishthira to perform the *Rajasuya yagya*. Yudhishthira called Shri Krishna to Indraprastha and held consultations with him regarding the *Rajasuya yagya*. Shri Krishna said to Yudhishthira, "Jarasandha has imprisoned thousands of kings with a view to performing the *Naramedha yagya*. He will not accept your supremacy. Therefore, you will have to kill him first and release the imprisoned kings. Only then will you be able to perform the *Rajasuya yagya*."

The story of the birth of Jarasandha is a strange one.

The valiant ruler of Magadha, King Bruhadratha, had married the two daughters of the King of Kashi. He did not have any child of his own. Therefore, he went into the forest and performed harsh penance. One day, a sage called Kaushika Muni gave him a mango fruit and said, "Give this mango to your wife. If she eats it, she will surely give birth to a son."

Bruhadratha cut the mango into two equal halves and gave one each to his two queens. In due course, the queens gave birth to sons, each with half the body. When the king saw the ugly babies, he got them tied in a cloth and ordered the bundle to be thrown in a heap of garbage. A demoness named Jara picked up the bundle with the hope to get some flesh to eat. The moment she touched the babies, the two halves were joined together and there was one complete beautiful baby. Jara transformed herself into a beautiful woman and went to the king and gave him the baby.

The baby came to be known as Jarasandha — the one who was joined by Jara, the demoness. Jarasandha grew up to be a very strong and mighty king.

Taking Yudhishthira's permission, Shri Krishna, Bheema and Arjuna disguised themselves as Brahmins and reached the capital of Jarasandha's kingdom. Jarasandha welcomed them and asked them the reason for their coming there. Disclosing his true identity, Shri Krishna challenged him, "We have come here to challenge you to a duel. You must fight a duel with any one of us."

Jarasandha said, "O Krishna! You are a cowherd and Arjuna is still very young. Therefore, I cannot fight a wrestling duel with either of you. I have heard a lot about Bheema's strength and valour. I am prepared to fight a duel with him."

Bheema and Jarasandha fought a duel for thirteen days. Jarasandha was tired on the fourteenth day. Shri Krishna gestured to Bheema to tear Jarasandha's body apart into two pieces. Bheema hurled Jarasandha on the ground, caught him by his leg and tore him apart into two pieces. Bheema was overjoyed at the death of Jarasandha. Meanwhile, the two parts of Jarasandha's body, once again, joined together. Jarasandha came back to life and started fighting the duel with Bheema once again. Bheema was puzzled and he looked at Shri Krishna for help. Shri Krishna took a leaf in his hand, split it vertically and threw the two pieces in opposite directions. Bheema understood Shri Krishna's hint. Once again, he tore Jarasandha's body apart and threw the two pieces in opposite directions. Thus, Jarasandha was dead.

Shri Krishna released all the kings imprisoned by Jarasandha. He then handed over the reins of the kingdom to Jarasandha's son Sahadeva and returned to Indraprastha along with Bheema and Arjuna.

97

25. THE SLAYING OF SHISHUPALA

After slaying Jarasandha, Shri Krishna, Bheema and Arjuna returned to Indraprastha. Later, Bheema, Arjuna, Nakula and Sahadeva went to the east, the north, the south and the west respectively to conquer the kingdoms there. All the kings accepted the supremacy of Yudhishthira. Thereafter, the *Rajasuya yagya* began at an auspicious time.

Many kings from all over the country and abroad came to attend the *Rajasuya yagya*. Bhishma, Dhritarashtra, Vidura, Drona, Kripacharya, Ashwatthama, Duryodhana and Dusshasana also came to attend the *yagya*. The *yagya* was completed as planned.

The *agrapooja* ceremony was a part of the completion of the *yagya* according to the Vedic rites. Bhishma said to Yudhishthira, "Shri Krishna is the best king among all those who are present here. Therefore, he should be worshipped first."

Sahadeva began to wash Shri Krishna's feet to worship him. Shishupala, the King of Chedi, was jealous of Shri Krishna. He began to hurl verbal abuses at Bhishma and Shri Krishna. Duryodhana was pleased at this. When Bheema realized this, he was agitated and came forward to tackle Shishupala. But Bhishma stopped Bheema and pacified him.

Shishupala was Shri Krishna's cousin. Shri Krishna had promised his aunt that he would forgive a hundred misdeeds of Shishupala. Therefore, Shri Krishna sat patiently and kept his cool till Shishupala hurled a hundred abusive words at him. But, Shishupala did not stop there. He continued to verbally abuse Shri Krishna. At last, Shri Krishna wielded his *Sudarshanchakra* and chopped off Shishupala's head. The whole assembly was stunned. Yudhishthira prayed to Shri Krishna to calm himself down. After the completion of *agrapooja*, Yudhishthira bid farewell to all the kings who had participated in the *yagya*. Yudhishthira crowned Shishupala's son Dhrishtaketu the King of Chedi.

Duryodhana was amazed to see the extraordinary architecture of the palace constructed by Maya. He, along with Shakuni, went round to see the palace.

As Duryodhana was walking round the palace, he came to a spot where, due to an optical illusion, it appeared to him that there was water. So he lifted his *dhoti* and began to wade across carefully. Actually it was not water, but the crystal floor. Duryodhana was embarrassed. Seeing this, Draupadi laughed at him. Duryodhana proceeded without uttering a word. On his way, he came across a wall made of transparent glass. Duryodhana did not realize this and he went ahead when suddenly, his head struck against the wall. Bheema who witnessed this sight, burst out laughing. Once again, Duryodhana was put in an embarrassing situation. Seeing this, Draupadi remarked, "The blind son of a blind father!"

Hearing these words, Duryodhana said to himself, "Henceforth, I will be careful not to make any such mistakes." As he went a little further, he came to a pond filled with crystal clear water. But, due to an optical illusion, it appeared like beautiful crystal floor. Duryodhana continued walking when suddenly, he fell into the pond with a splash. All the people who were present there burst out laughing. Duryodhana was greatly ashamed and embarrassed. Immediately, he took his leave of Yudhishthira and left for Hastinapur along with Shakuni.

26. THE GAME OF DICE

On returning to Hastinapur, Duryodhana said to Dhritarashtra, "Yudhishthira has constructed a magnificent palace in Indraprastha. I have no words to describe its grandeur."

Duryodhana also told him that Draupadi had called him 'the blind son of a blind father'. These words of Draupadi hurt Dhritarashtra and he felt humiliated. Taking advantage of the opportunity, Duryodhana said to Dhritarashtra, "Father! I have a plan. Shakuni uncle is an expert in the game of dice. Yudhishthira is also fond of playing this game. If you invite him for a game of dice, he will not refuse. We will win their kingdom by defeating them in the game of dice and thus, we can avenge our insult."

After having heard the insulting words of Draupadi, Dhritarashtra, too, was burning with rage. He wanted to avenge his insult. Yet, he sought Vidura's advice on the proposal put forward by Duryodhana. Vidura advised him, "The game of dice is the root of all evils. Do not allow Duryodhana to play this game."

Yet, Duryodhana succeeded in convincing Dhritarashtra to invite Yudhishthira for a game of dice.

Vidura went to Indraprastha and gave Dhritarashtra's message to Yudhishthira. At the same time, he said to Yudhishthira, "The invitation for a game of dice is an evil scheme by Duryodhana. If possible, I request you not to come to Hastinapur."

Yudhishthira himself was fond of playing the game of dice. Therefore, he ignored Vidura's advice and reached Hastinapur along with his brothers and Draupadi. The Pandavas bowed to Bhishma, Dhritarashtra, Gandhari and other elders. The Kauravas warmly embraced the Pandavas and welcomed them. Special arrangements were made for their stay in Hastinapur. After dinner, the Pandavas slept peacefully.

The following day, Yudhishthira, accompanied by his brothers, arrived in a hall specially constructed for the game of dice. Family elders like Bhishma, Drona, Kripacharya, Vidura and Dhritarashtra were also present in the hall. The game began. Shakuni resorted to unfair means and cheating while throwing the dice in order to benefit Duryodhana. Yudhishthira lost one game after another. He staked everything he had and gradually lost all his wealth, his kingdom, his servants, brothers and at last his own self. In the end, Duryodhana and Shakuni persuaded him to stake Draupadi. Yudhishthira lost that game, too.

Duryodhana was jubilant and exhilarated. The Pandavas had lost everything in the game of dice. Having won the kingdom of the Pandavas, Duryodhana was intoxicated with the pride of his victory. He ordered Chief Minister Vidura,

"Go at once and bring Draupadi here. Since we have won her in the game of dice, she will work as a maid in our palace."

A furious Vidura reprimanded Duryodhana and left the gambling hall. Duryodhana then asked his youngest brother Vikarna to bring Draupadi into the gambling hall. Vikarna went to Draupadi and told her about Duryodhana's order. Draupadi was shocked to hear about what had happened during the game of dice. She said to Vikarna, "If King Yudhishthira had already lost his own self in the game of dice, he had no right to stake me. Go back to the gambling hall and repeat my words to all those who are present there."

Vikarna returned to the gambling hall and repeated Draupadi's words in front of the whole assembly. On hearing this, Yudhishthira was rendered speechless. An agitated and furious Duryodhana ordered his brother Dusshasana,

"Do what you please; but you must bring Draupadi into this gambling hall right now."

Dusshasana walked towards Draupadi's room in order to bring her into the gambling hall.

27. SHRI KRISHNA COMES TO DRAUPADI'S RESCUE

Dusshasana entered Draupadi's room and rudely ordered her to come to the gambling hall. Draupadi said, "I am the daughter-in-law of this family. Your mutual hatred and jealousy should not cost me my self-respect and dignity."

When Dusshasana began to misbehave with her and force her to go with him, she ran towards Gandhari's room. Dusshasana followed her, caught her by her hair and dragged her into the gambling hall. Bhishma, Drona and Kripacharya hung their heads in shame. Tears began to roll down the cheeks of the helpless Draupadi. A furious Bheema roared like a lion, "In the presence of Surya, the Sun-god and all the other gods, I vow that I will sever the dirty hands with which Dusshasana has dared to touch Draupadi's hair and I will tear open his chest and drink his blood."

Hearing the roaring words of the enraged Bheema, the Kauravas began to tremble with fear.

Duryodhana patted his thigh and gestured to Draupadi to come and sit on it. Now Bheema could no longer control himself. He said to Duryodhana, "O wicked Duryodhana! One day, with a blow of my mace, I will break the thigh on which you have gestured to Draupadi to sit."

Hearing Bheema's warning, Duryodhana was furious. He said to Dusshasana, "We have won Draupadi in the game of dice. Therefore, she is our maid now. The clothes of a queen do not befit a maid. I order you to strip her of her royal clothes."

A defenceless Draupadi pleaded with everyone in the gambling hall to protect her honour and dignity. But fearing Duryodhana, none dared to come to her rescue. They could not stop Duryodhana from humiliating and dishonouring Draupadi. A disappointed Draupadi prayed to Shri Krishna, "O Lord! Now you are my only hope and I surrender myself to you. Please protect my honour and dignity."

Dusshasana caught one end of Draupadi's saree and began to pull it. Once again, the elders sitting in the hall hung their heads in shame.

An invisible Shri Krishna responded to Draupadi's cries for help. He made Draupadi's saree so long that its end could not be found. Dusshasana went on pulling one saree after the other, but there appeared to be no end to the saree. Soon there was a heap of sarees in the hall. But, the saree worn by Draupadi was still as it was. The whole assembly was stunned to see this miracle. Now, Dusshasana was also tired of pulling Draupadi's sarees. He was so exhausted that he almost fainted. At last, he fell down in a corner of the gambling hall. There was an utter stillness in the hall. Everybody was absolutely speechless. At that time, Bheema flew into a towering rage. He roared,

"O people gathered in this assembly! Listen to my vow. I vow that I will not leave the earth until and unless I have torn open the chest of this wicked Dusshasana and drunk his blood."

Hearing Bheema's vow, everybody in the assembly began to tremble with fear. A horrified and anxious Dhritarashtra called Yudhishthira to him and said, "Son! You are wise, kind and generous. You have a big heart. Please forgive Duryodhana for his wickedness. I return to you all that you have lost in the game of dice. Go back to Indraprastha and rule your kingdom happily."

The Pandavas were satisfied and pacified with the kind words and behaviour of Dhritarashtra. They bowed to him and returned to Indraprastha along with Draupadi. On their way, Draupadi said to Bheema, "In spite of having five valiant husbands, none could protect my honour and dignity. If Shri Krishna would not have come to my rescue at the right time, it would have been very difficult for me to lead a normal life."

28. THE PANDAVAS' EXILE

Dhritarashtra returned to Yudhishthira his kingdom, wealth, army, servants and whatever he had lost in the game of dice. Therefore, Duryodhana was disappointed. Angry and hurt, he spoke very bitterly and rudely to Dhritarashtra. Ultimately, Duryodhana prevailed upon Dhritarashtra to once again invite Yudhishthira for a game of dice.

When the Pandavas and Draupadi reached Indraprastha, a messenger of Dhritarashtra was already present there. He gave Yudhishthira Dhritarashtra's message. Yudhishthira's counsellors clearly advised him against accepting the invitation to play a game of dice again. But Yudhishthira ignored their advice. He thought that as a man with self-respect he had to accept the challenge to play a game of dice. Therefore, Yudhishthira, along with his brothers, went to Hastinapur. The following condition was laid down for the game :

'The one who loses the game of dice will go into exile for twelve years and then live incognito for one year. But if he is found out or recognized during his life incognito, he will have to go into exile for another twelve years.'

This time, too, Duryodhana and Shakuni resorted to unfair means and cheating to defeat Yudhishthira in the game of dice.

According to the condition laid down, the Pandavas had to go into exile. Yudhishthira sent Kunti to Vidura's house. Arjuna's wife Subhadra, along with Abhimanyu and Draupadi's sons, went to Dwarika.

The Pandavas and Draupadi began their journey into exile. The Brahmins and the other people of Hastinapur also began to follow them. They condemned and denounced Duryodhana and Dhritarashtra. However, Yudhishthira, with great difficulty, consoled them and convinced them to return to Hastinapur. But some Brahmins were not prepared to leave Yudhishthira and hence, they accompanied the Pandavas into exile.

One day, when Dhritarashtra and Vidura were having some discussion, Narada Muni came there and said to Dhritarashtra, "Exactly fourteen years from now, the entire Kaurava dynasty will be completely destroyed. As a result of Duryodhana's sins, the name of the Kauravas will be totally wiped out from the earth."

Saying this, Narada disappeared. Dhritarashtra was very worried. Duryodhana and his allies, too, were terrified on hearing Narada Muni's prophecy. They said to Dronacharya, "*Gurudev*! Come what may, but please always remain with us."

The Pandavas and the Brahmins reached a forest. On the advice of their family priest Dhaumya, Yudhishthira began to worship Surya, the Sun-god. The Sun-god was pleased with his worship and appeared before him. He gave Yudhishthira a vessel which would always remain full of food. Every morning, the vessel would give as much food as was required. It went on giving food till it was cleaned and washed. Draupadi fed the Pandavas and the Brahmins from that vessel every day. In the end, she would have her share and then wash the vessel clean. Wandering through the forests, the Pandavas reached a forest called Kamyakavana on the banks of the river Saraswati. The Pandavas lived happily in the forest. Many sages would often come and stay with them. The preachings of the sages and other learned men not only gave the Pandavas immense knowledge but also inspired them to lead their life with courage and patience. The sages also told them stories of Nala-Damayanti, Agastya-Lopamudra, Rushyashringa, Ashtavakra and others.

113

One day, Shri Krishna and King Drupada of Panchal came to meet the Pandavas in the Kamyakavana. Shri Krishna consoled the Pandavas. Later, King Drupada and Shri Krishna took their leave of the Pandavas. After some time, Maharshi Vyasa came there and said to Yudhishthira, "After the thirteen years of exile, there will be a terrible war between you and the Kauravas. Therefore, start preparing for the war right away. Acquire as many divine weapons as you can from the gods. Arjuna will have to go to Mount Kailas and acquire the *Pashupatastra* from Lord Shiva. Without these divine weapons, you will not be able to fight the war against great warriors like Bhishma and Dronacharya."

29. ARJUNA ACQUIRES DIVINE WEAPONS

On the advice of Maharshi Vyasa, the Pandavas began to make the necessary preparations for the war. Yudhishthira immediately sent Arjuna to Mount Kailas. Draupadi wished Arjuna good luck so that he might succeed in his mission.

Arjuna took his leave of his brothers and Draupadi and set off on an arduous journey. Arjuna was the master of *Pratismriti*. With the help of the knowledge of *Pratismriti*, Arjuna could travel at the speed of thoughts. So, in a matter of a few seconds, Arjuna reached the foot of the Himalayas and crossed Mount Gandhamadana to reach Mount Indrakeel. An ascetic, who sat there in meditation, said to Arjuna, "Who are you and where have you come from? This is the land for practising penance. You cannot roam here with weapons."

Arjuna bowed to the ascetic and said, "I am Arjuna, the son of King Pandu of Hastinapur. I have not yet relinquished my duties as a Kshatriya. Therefore, I cannot move around without weapons in an unknown land."

The ascetic was pleased with Arjuna's reply and said, "Arjuna! I am Indra. You may ask for a boon and it will be granted to you."

Arjuna said, "Please give me your divine weapons."

Lord Indra said, "First, you must go to Mount Kailas and invoke Lord Shiva to acquire the *Pashupatastra* from him. Only after that, will all the gods bless you with their divine weapons."

Arjuna went to Mount Kailas and performed harsh penance to invoke Lord Shiva. After some days, Lord Shiva, disguised as a *Bhil*, came there to test Arjuna. Lord Shiva was accompanied by Parvati and hundreds of his servants, the *ganas*. At that very moment, Lord Shiva spotted a demon called Mooka, who was moving in the form of a boar. Mooka was rushing towards Arjuna in order to attack him. At once, Lord Shiva aimed and shot an arrow at the boar. But, at the same time, an arrow from Arjuna's bow also hit the boar. The boar fell down dead. Arjuna did not recognize Lord Shiva who was disguised as a *Bhil*. He asked him, "How dare you shoot an arrow at my game?"

Lord Shiva said, "I had aimed and shot an arrow before you did. Thus, this is not your game, but mine."

Saying this, the *Bhil* burst out laughing. Arjuna felt insulted. He shot innumerable arrows at the *Bhil* in order to teach him a lesson. But the arrows did not have any effect on the *Bhil's* body. The *Bhil* stood there smiling! Arjuna then attacked him with a sword. The *Bhil* broke Arjuna's sword into pieces. At last, Arjuna challenged the *Bhil* to a duel. After a long duel, Arjuna was tired and he fell down. Sitting down on the ground, Arjuna worshipped an idol of Lord Shiva and put a garland of flowers around it. He then got up to continue the duel with the *Bhil*. But, he was surprised to see the same garland around the *Bhil's* neck, too. When Arjuna turned around and looked at the idol of Lord Shiva, he did not see the garland there. Immediately, Arjuna fell at the feet of the *Bhil*. He now realized that the *Bhil* was none other than Lord Shiva himself. Lord Shiva asked Arjuna to ask for a boon. Arjuna asked for the *Pashupatastra*. Lord Shiva said, "*Tathastu*! Your boon is granted. But you will never use the *Pashupatastra* against any human being."

Arjuna then sought the blessings of Parvati. Lord Shiva and Parvati blessed Arjuna and disappeared along with the *ganas*.

30. ARJUNA IN *INDRALOKA*, THE KINGDOM OF LORD INDRA

After Lord Shiva and Parvati had disappeared, Maatali, the charioteer of Lord Indra, came to Arjuna along with Lord Indra's divine chariot. He said, "Lord Indra and the other gods are eagerly awaiting your arrival in heaven. You have to help Lord Indra destroy the *asuras*, the arch enemies of gods."

Arjuna was mighty pleased to know that Lord Indra had invited him and so he sat in the divine chariot. Maatali drove the chariot at an incredible speed and reached Arjuna to heaven. Lord Indra, Yama, Varuna, Agni and many other gods, *gandharvas* and *apsaras* stood at the doors of heaven to welcome Arjuna. The *apsaras* led Arjuna to a beautifully decorated palace.

All the gods in heaven gave their divine weapons to Arjuna. A fierce battle was then fought between the gods and the *asuras*. Arjuna was a big help to the gods. Everybody in *Indraloka* praised Arjuna's skills and valour highly. During his five year long stay in heaven, Arjuna acquired the knowledge of the use of the divine weapons. He learnt music from Chitrasena, the king of the *gandharvas*. Arjuna also learnt the art of dancing from Urvashi, an *apsara*.

One night, Urvashi came to Arjuna and sat beside him on his bed. At once, Arjuna got up and said, "O Mother! Why did you take the trouble of coming here? You could have sent for me and I would have promptly presented myself in your service."

"Parth! An *apsara* of heaven can never be anyone's mother or sister. I have come here to win your love," said Urvashi.

Arjuna, in a kind voice, said, "O *apsara*! Lord Indra is my *guru*. Since you are an *apsara* in his court, I revere you as a mother. And, I have learnt the art of dancing from you. Therefore, you, too, are my *guru*, I have come here as a student. It is a student's duty to work hard to gain knowledge. Therefore, I pray you to grant me your favours and blessings."

Urvashi tried her best to lure Arjuna, but it was all in vain. Arjuna remained unshakeable. At last, Urvashi was enraged and she cursed Arjuna,

"You have insulted my beauty and so, I curse you that you will have to live on the earth as a woman for one year. But you have honoured me by revering me as a mother. Hence, my curse will, in fact, prove to be a boon for you."

Meanwhile, Arjuna's long absence was a cause of worry for Yudhishthira and the other brothers. One day, Narada came to them and said, "Maharshi Lomash will come here from heaven. He will give you the news about Arjuna."

After some days, Maharshi Lomash came to meet the Pandavas. Giving them the news about Arjuna, he said, "Arjuna performed harsh penance to please Lord Shiva and hence, he has succeeded in procuring the *Pashupatastra*. All the gods, too, have given him their divine weapons. At present, Arjuna is learning music and dance from the *gandharvas* and the *apsaras*. He misses you a lot and fondly remembers you."

The Pandavas were relieved to hear the news about Arjuna and his success. They said to Maharshi Lomash, "Narada has asked us to go on a pilgrimage. We will be grateful to you, if you could take us on a pilgrimage."

Maharshi Lomash took the Pandavas to many places of pilgrimage. The Pandavas were delighted.

31. THE ADVENTURES OF BHEEMA AND ARJUNA

One day, when Bheema was wandering in a forest, he came across Hanuman. Hanuman blessed Bheema and said, "During the war between you and the Kauravas, I will be present on the flag of Arjuna's chariot. You will be victorious in that war."

After some days, Arjuna returned from heaven and came back to the Pandavas. He had brought with him the *Pashupatastra* and many other divine weapons. The Pandavas were delighted with his success.

One day, the Pandavas went on a hunting trip into a forest. In their absence, King Jayadratha of Sindhu entered the Pandavas' *ashram* and abducted Draupadi. When the Pandavas returned to the *ashram*, they came to know about Jayadratha's sinful deed. Bheema and Arjuna chased Jayadratha and caught him alive. Jayadratha saved his life by apologizing to Yudhishthira and Draupadi. Jayadratha wanted to avenge this insult by the Pandavas. Hence, he performed harsh penance to please Lord Shiva. After some time, Lord Shiva appeared before him to bless him and said, "None of the Pandavas, except Arjuna, can ever defeat you."

One day, Duryodhana, accompanied by his queens, Karna, Shakuni and a huge army, came to the Kamyakavana. Duryodhana had with him silver and golden chariots studded with pearls, diamonds and rubies, and elephants with seats studded with precious stones. The Pandavas lived in a *parnakuti* (small cottage) on the banks of a lake in the Kamyakavana. Duryodhana's only aim was to hurt the Pandavas by showing off his wealth, riches and grandeur.

Duryodhana got his tents pitched in a large open ground. He went on hunting trips every day and spent his days enjoying himself in worldly pleasures. One day, Duryodhana wanted to bathe in a nearby lake. He sent his servants to make arrangements for a swim in the lake. At that time, Chitrasena, the king of the *gandharvas* was already there along with the other *gandharvas* and *apsaras*. The *gandharvas* threatened Duryodhana's servants and scared them away. Duryodhana sent his army to teach the *gandharvas* a lesson. Duryodhana's soldiers said to the *gandharvas*, "Leave this spot and go to some other place. Duryodhana, the crown prince of Hastinapur, is coming here for a bath."

Chitrasena and the other *gandharvas* attacked Duryodhana's army and drove the soldiers away from that spot. At last, Duryodhana came there along with Karna and Shakuni. A fierce battle ensued between them and the *gandharvas*. Karna showered a volley of arrows at the *gandharvas*. The frightened *gandharvas* started running helter-skelter to save their lives. Chitrasena, at once, came to their rescue. With a fiercer volley of arrows,

he defeated the army of Duryodhana. When the soldiers began to flee, Chitrasena used the *Sammohan astra*. As a result, the soldiers fell down unconscious. Chitrasena then broke Karna's chariot. Karna sat in another chariot and fled from the scene. Chitrasena captured Duryodhana and his queens, put them in a chariot and drove towards heaven.

Duryodhana's minister went to the *parnakuti* to inform Yudhishthira about the incident. When Bheema heard the details of the incident, he was mighty pleased. Yudhishthira said to Bheema and Arjuna, "It is, indeed, a matter of great shame for us that Chitrasena has captured and imprisoned the women of our family. Under normal circumstances we five brothers are against the hundred Kauravas. But when somebody else, an outsider, attacks even one of our brothers, we are a hundred and five brothers together. Please remember this well. Now, I command you to rescue them and bring them here."

Obeying the order of their elder brother, Bheema and Arjuna began to chase Chitrasena, the king of the *gandharvas*. With the help of the *Mahakarshan astra*, Arjuna brought Chitrasena's chariot down to the earth. Chitrasena was aware of Arjuna's divine powers. He did not wish to fight against Arjuna and so, he set Duryodhana and his queens free. Arjuna and Chitrasena met each other cordially. Chitrasena said to Arjuna, "Duryodhana, the great sinner, had come to the Kamyakavana with the sole aim of harassing you. Therefore, I had to punish him. You have shown your grace and dignity by setting them free. But Duryodhana doesn't deserve it."

Duryodhana was placed in a very disgraceful position. Though his queens expressed their gratitude and thanked Bheema and Arjuna, Duryodhana could not utter a word. He then left for Hastinapur along with his queens.

32. KARNA DONATES HIS *KAVACHA* AND *KUNDALS*

During the battle against the *gandharvas*, Karna had to flee from the battlefield in order to save his life. Meanwhile, Bheema and Arjuna rescued Duryodhana and freed him and his queens from the clutches of Chitrasena. As a result, Karna became more jealous of the Pandavas. With a view to defeating Arjuna in a war, he began to perform harsh penance to please the Sun-god. This worried Lord Indra a lot because Karna was born with the *kavacha* and the *kundals* which had made him invincible. Therefore, Lord Indra made up his mind to go to Karna and ask for his *kavacha* and *kundals*.

Karna was the son of Surya, the Sun-god. When Lord Surya came to know about Lord Indra's plan, he was worried and anxious to protect Karna's life. Lord Surya appeared in Karna's dream and warned him,

"Lord Indra, in the disguise of a Brahmin, will come to you and ask you to donate your *kavacha*

and *kundals*. Therefore, beware of him. Do not part with your *kavacha* and *kundals*."

Karna said to Lord Surya, "I have vowed that anyone who comes to me with a request for something will never return empty-handed. I am ready to lay down my life for the sake of fulfilling my vow."

Lord Surya was disappointed with Karna's reply.

The following morning, when Karna was worshipping Lord Surya on the banks of the river Ganga, Lord Indra came to him in the form of a Brahmin. As Karna turned around after worshipping Lord Surya, he spotted the Brahmin. He remembered his dream and immediately recognized the Brahmin to be none other than Lord Indra himself. Karna smiled at the Brahmin and asked him, "O learned man! What brings you here? What do you want from me?"

Lord Indra, who was disguised as a Brahmin, asked Karna to give him his *kavacha* and *kundals*. Karna, at once, took a knife, separated the *kavacha* and *kundals* from his body and placed them in Lord Indra's hands.

Impressed with Karna's generosity, Lord Indra said, "Karna! I have never seen a great and generous donor like you before. I am Indra. You may ask for anything except the *Vajra*."

Karna said to Lord Indra, "I do not want anything except your *Amogha Shakti* (infallible weapon)."

Lord Indra granted Karna his *Amogha Shakti* and said, "The person against whom you will use this *Amogha Shakti* will surely lose his life. But, you can use this power only once, after which it will come back to me."

Karna was overwhelmed on acquiring the *Amogha Shakti*. He made up his mind and said to himself, "When the time comes, I will use the *Amogha Shakti* against Arjuna." Lord Indra blessed Karna and left.

33. *YAKSHA'S* QUESTIONS

After the incident of Draupadi's abduction by Jayadratha, the Pandavas had left the Kamyakavana and were now living in the Dwaitavana. One day, a Brahmin came there and requested the Pandavas, "A wooden stick used to kindle a fire hung from a tree in the compound of my hut. A deer came there and started rubbing its head against the stick. Unfortunately, the stick got entangled in the deer's horns and the frightened deer ran away into the forest along with the stick. Will you please chase the deer and get back my stick for me?"

The Pandavas pitied the poor Brahmin and so they chased the deer. But suddenly, the deer escaped and disappeared into the thick forest. Tired, the Pandavas sat down to rest for some time under a banyan tree in the forest.

After the long chase, the Pandavas were thirsty. Yudhishthira sent Nakula to bring some water to drink. Wandering in search of water, Nakula soon reached a small lake. Suddenly, he heard a voice,

"O son of Madri! I am a *yaksha* (a demi-god) and this lake belongs to me. You can drink as much water as you want to from this lake; but first, you must answer my questions."

Nakula, however, did not pay any attention to the *yaksha's* warning. He entered the lake and quenched his thirst. He then took some water for his brothers and came out of the lake. But, as soon as he reached the banks of the lake, he fell down unconscious on the ground.

Meanwhile, since Nakula had not returned, a worried Yudhishthira sent Sahadeva in search of Nakula. Many hours passed, but there was no sign of Sahadeva, too. An anxious Yudhishthira was dying of thirst. At last, he sent Arjuna to search for Nakula and Sahadeva.

When Arjuna reached the lake, he saw Nakula and Sahadeva lying there unconscious. Arjuna, too, heard the voice of an invisible man. He shot many arrows in the direction of the voice, but it was all in vain. Arjuna then entered the water and quenched his thirst. But, like his brothers, the moment he came to the bank, he fell down unconscious. Meanwhile, after waiting for a long time, Bheema set off in search of his three brothers. When he reached the lake, he saw Nakula, Sahadeva and Arjuna lying unconscious on the bank. Bheema was deeply moved by the plight of his three brothers. However, when the thirsty Bheema entered the lake to drink some water, he heard the voice,

"O valiant Bheema! You cannot drink water from this lake unless you answer my questions. If you do not fulfil this condition, you, too, will meet with the same fate as your brothers did."

An angry Bheema roared, "You cruel man! Who are you? How dare you threaten me like a coward? If you have the courage to face me, I will teach you the lesson of your life."

Saying this, Bheema quenched his thirst. But, as soon as he reached the bank, he, too, fell down unconscious.

When Bheema, too, did not return for a long time, Yudhishthira got extremely anxious and worried about his brothers. Tired of a long wait, Yudhishthira himself set off in search of his brothers. When he came to the banks of the lake, he saw his four brothers lying there unconscious. Yudhishthira was pained to see his brothers' plight. He made up his mind to quench his thirst and then begin his search for the enemy. No sooner did Yudhishthira step into the water than he heard the voice,

"Beware, O Yudhishthira! I am a *yaksha* and I own this lake. Your brothers did not obey me and so they are lying here in this helpless condition. If you want to drink water from this lake, you must answer my questions first. Unless you obey me, you will suffer the same fate as your brothers did."

Yudhishthira addressed the voice and said, "Please ask your questions. I will try to answer them to the best of my knowledge and ability."

The *yaksha* asked some questions to Yudhishthira and Yudhishthira answered them as follows :

Yaksha : Who is man's best friend?

Yudhishthira : Patience.

Yaksha : Who can run faster than the wind?

Yudhishthira : Thoughts.

Yaksha : Who is the greatest enemy of man?

Yudhishthira : Anger.

Yaksha : Which loss makes man richer?

Yudhishthira : Man becomes richer after losing his greed.

Yaksha : Which is the greatest wonder of the world?

Yudhishthira : Thousands of human beings die every day. In spite of knowing this fact, the people of the world wish to live eternally!

The *yaksha* asked many such questions and Yudhishthira answered them satisfactorily. At last, the *yaksha* appeared before Yudhishthira and said, "I am pleased with your answers. In return, I will bring one of your brothers back to life."

Yudhishthira requested the *yaksha* to bring Nakula back to life. The *yaksha* asked him the reason for choosing none but Nakula. Yudhishthira replied, "My father, King Pandu, had two wives. Of Kunti's three sons, I am still alive. I wish that one of the sons of my father's second wife Madri should also be alive. Therefore, I request you to bring back to life Nakula, the son of Madri."

The *yaksha* was very pleased to see Yudhishthira's love for justice. He brought all the four brothers back to life. After blessing Yudhishthira, the *yaksha* disappeared.

34. THE PANDAVAS LIVE INCOGNITO

The Pandavas completed their twelve years in exile. Now they were to live incognito for one year. If Duryodhana found them out during this one year, the Pandavas had to go into exile for another twelve years. After long deliberations, the Pandavas decided to spend this one crucial year in Viratnagar, the capital of the Matsya kingdom. Yudhishthira said to his brothers and Draupadi, "I will go to the court of King Virata and live there as a Brahmin named 'Kanka'. I will entertain the king with various games like gambling and chess and also hold intelligent discussions with him. Bheema will work in the royal kitchen as 'Ballava', the cook. Arjuna will disguise himself as a woman called 'Brihannala' and teach music and dance to the Princess of Viratnagar. Nakula will call himself 'Granthika' and work as a horsegroom in the royal stable. Sahadeva, as 'Tantripala', will look after the royal cow-shed. Draupadi will live with the Queen of Viratnagar as 'Sairandhri', the royal maid. In this way, we will all be able to live together in the same place."

The Pandavas hid their weapons in the branches of the *Shami* tree on the outskirts of Viratnagar. As decided, they then disguised themselves and entered Viratnagar by different routes. All of them, one by one, approached King Virata as Kanka, Ballava, Brihannala, Granthika and Tantripala. The king employed all of them in his service.

Draupadi, disguised as a maid, went to Sudeshna, the Queen of Viratnagar. Sudeshna was impressed with Draupadi's beauty and grace. She said, "Who are you? Why have you come here?"

Draupadi replied, "My fate has brought me here. My name is Sairandhri. I am the wife of five *gandharvas*. They serve the gods. I am skilled in the art of hair-style and make-up. Therefore, I have come to live with you as your maid; but on one condition : I will not touch any used utensils or eat any leftovers. If I do not fulfil this condition, my husbands will be angry with me. Though they remain invisible, they always protect me."

Impressed by Draupadi's magnetic personality, Sudeshna readily agreed to the condition laid down by her and employed her as her personal maid.

35. THE SLAYING OF KEECHAKA

Keechaka, the brother of Queen Sudeshna, was the Commander-in-Chief of King Virat's army. Being strong and powerful, he greatly influenced the administration of the kingdom. One day, he spotted Sairandhri. Keechaka was struck by her beauty and charm. He was so fascinated by her grace and elegance that he decided to win her over at any cost. Keechaka inquired with his sister Sudeshna about Sairandhri. But Sudeshna did not give him any information. At last, Keechaka went to Sairandhri and said, "O beautiful maiden! I am fascinated by your beauty and charm. If you marry me, you will be duly honoured like Queen Sudeshna."

Sairandhri was shocked and frightened on hearing Keechaka's indecent demand. She said, "I am an ordinary maid. I am already married and so, please do not repeat these words to me ever again."

Keechaka was desperate to win Sairandhri over. Now Sudeshna was also ready to help her brother in his evil endeavours. One day, a big celebration was organized in the kingdom. Sudeshna sent her maid Sairandhri to Keechaka's palace under the pretext of getting some wine from there. When Sairandhri was returning from Keechaka's palace with the wine, Keechaka stopped her on the way and cornered her. At that time, in order to free herself from the clutches of Keechaka, Sairandhri said, "I am ready to surrender myself to you. But my husbands, the five *gandharvas*, who always remain invisible, protect me. They should never come to know of my meeting with you. Therefore, I cannot meet you in your palace. I will wait for you in the dance-hall tonight."

Keechaka was overjoyed to hear these words from Sairandhri. He eagerly waited for the sun to set that day. Sairandhri delivered the wine to Sudeshna and immediately went to meet Bheema. She narrated the whole incident to Bheema. Bheema said, "Do not worry. Go to sleep peacefully tonight. I will go to the dance-hall and take care of Keechaka."

That night, Keechaka, decked in his best clothes, came to meet Sairandhri in the dance-hall. Bheema had draped himself in a saree and was lying on a cot in the hall. It was dark inside the hall. And so, Keechaka took Bheema for Sairandhri and warmly embraced him. At once, Bheema got up and pounced on Keechaka. After a violent duel, Bheema killed Keechaka.

The following morning, the news of Keechaka's death spread all over the kingdom. King Virata and Queen Sudeshna were deeply shocked at his sudden death. Sudeshna asked Sairandhri, "Who has killed Keechaka? Do you know anything about his murder?"

Sairandhri replied, "I told you that my five invisible husbands, the *gandharvas*, always protect me. I had warned your brother about his indecent behaviour with me, but he ignored my warning. Hence, I think the *gandharvas* must have killed him."

Hearing Sairandhri's words, Sudeshna started trembling with fear. She said, "Sairandhri! If, because of you, your husbands make us the targets of their rage, we will be totally destroyed. Therefore, please go away to some other kingdom."

Sairandhri said, "It is my duty to obey you. But please give me one month's time to find another job for myself. I promise to leave within a month."

Sudeshna agreed. However, she said, "But, you must see to it that your husbands, the *gandharvas*, do not harm the King and my son Prince Uttar."

145

36. ARJUNA'S EXPLOITS AS BRIHANNALA

As per the conditions laid down, the Pandavas, after living in exile for twelve years, had to live incognito for one year. If they were found out or recognized during that particular year, they had to go into exile for another twelve years. So, as soon as the year of living incognito began, Duryodhana started making all possible attempts to trace the Pandavas. Duryodhana's spies were travelling in each and every kingdom of the country searching for the Pandavas. But Duryodhana could not trace the Pandavas. Meanwhile, one of Duryodhana's spies gave him the news of Keechaka's assassination. On hearing the news, Duryodhana presumed that the maid Sairandhri was Draupadi and that her five husbands, the *gandharvas*, were actually the Pandavas. Duryodhana was sure that only Bheema could kill Keechaka in a duel.

With a view to locating the Pandavas, Duryodhana decided to invade the Matsya kingdom of King Virata. At that time, King Susharma of Trigarta came to Duryodhana and said, "King Virata's Commander-in-Chief, Keechaka, had harassed me a lot. Now that he is dead, I will attack the Matsya kingdom from the south. While King Virat is engaged in a battle against my army, you can invade his kingdom from the north. Since that part of his kingdom will be unprotected, you can easily win the battle."

Duryodhana agreed with Susharma. Susharma attacked the Matsya kingdom from the south and captured innumerable cows. King Virata, with a heavy heart, remembered Keechaka. Consoling him, Kanka (Yudhishthira) said, "I am skilled in the art of warfare. I have heard that Ballava, Granthika and Tantripala can also fight a battle. If you give us chariots and weapons, we can help you in the battle. I assure you that you will be victorious in this battle."

King Virata provided Kanka, Ballava, Granthika and Tantripala with chariots and weapons and took them along with him to the battlefield. A fierce battle ensued between King Susharma of Trigarta and King Virata. Susharma broke King Virata's chariot and captured him. When Susharma was taking King Virata away, Bheema attacked him and freed King Virata. He then defeated Susharma and captured him as a prisoner. Susharma's soldiers started running helter-skelter to save their lives. At that time, King Virata's soldiers launched a fierce attack on them and forced them to flee the battlefield. King Virata won the battle against Susharma. When the news of their king's victory reached the people of the Matsya kingdom, they started making preparations to welcome him.

The whole kingdom was busy making preparations to celebrate the grand victory of their king. Meanwhile, Duryodhana invaded the Matsya kingdom from the north. His army destroyed all the fields on their way. They collected and captured thousands of Virata's cows. The cowherds came to Prince Uttar and pleaded with him to rescue their cows from the clutches of Duryodhana's soldiers. An enthusiastic Prince Uttar said to the cowherds, "If I get an able charioteer, I will fight a battle against Duryodhana and get your cows back for you."

Hearing this, Brihannala(Arjuna) said to Prince Uttar, "I had worked as Arjuna's charioteer. Prepare yourself for the battle. I will drive your chariot."

Prince Uttar entered the battlefield with Brihannala as his charioteer. He saw the brave warriors like Duryodhana, Bhishma, Drona, Kripacharya, Karna and Ashwatthama standing before him. When he realized how huge the army of Duryodhana was, he began to tremble with fear. He said to Brihannala, "Brihannala! Drive my chariot back to my palace. I do not want to fight this battle."

Brihannala said, "Do not be afraid. You do not have to fight this battle. I will fight this battle for you. But you must drive this chariot exactly according to my instructions."

Having said this, Arjuna, who was disguised as Brihannala, drove the chariot towards the *Shami* tree on the outskirts of Viratnagar. He then revealed his true identity to Uttar and took out his bow, the *gandeev*, from the *Shami* tree. Prince Uttar bowed to Arjuna and took the reins of the horses in his hands. He swiftly drove the chariot towards the battlefield and stopped it right in front of the Kaurava army.

Kripacharya said to Duryodhana, "This eunuch who thus dares to face valiant warriors like us, along with our huge army, appears to be Arjuna." At that moment there was a loud distinctive twang of Arjuna's bow, the *gandeev,* and he blew his conch, the *Devadatta.* Hearing these loud sounds, Duryodhana asked Bhishma *pitamaha,* "*Pitamaha*! Is the period for the Pandavas to live incognito over?"

Bhishma *pitamaha* replied, "Yes. That period was over yesterday."

Arjuna began to shower a volley of arrows from his *gandeev.* The whole army of the Kauravas was dispersed and the soldiers began to flee the battlefield. Arjuna killed Vikarna, the son of Karna. Karna, who was injured by Arjuna's arrows, had to flee the battlefield to save his life. Arjuna's arrows hit Drona and Bhishma in their chests and they fell down unconscious. Finally, Arjuna used the *Sammohan astra,* as a result of which the whole army of the Kauravas fell down unconscious. Prince Uttar took the colourful rich clothes and crowns of Dronacharya, Kripacharya, Ashwatthama and Duryodhana. Arjuna and Prince Uttar secured the cows of Virata and returned to Viratnagar.

When Duryodhana, Bhishma, Dronacharya, Kripacharya and other soldiers regained consciousness, they did not wish to fight the battle anymore. Hence, they returned to Hastinapur. When King Virata came to know that his son, Prince Uttar, had defeated the army of Duryodhana, his joy knew no bounds. He decided to hold victory celebrations in honour of the prince. It was then that Prince Uttar told his father King Virata about the exploits of Arjuna and revealed the true identities of the Pandavas and Draupadi. King Virata fell at Yudhishthira's feet and sought his forgiveness. Yudhishthira said to King Virata, "We are truly indebted to you because we have lived in your kingdom happily for the past twelve months."

King Virata gave his daughter Uttara's hand in marriage to Arjuna's son Abhimanyu. Later, he made the necessary arrangements for the Pandavas to stay in Upaplavya, a city in his kingdom.

37. ARJUNA SEEKS SHRI KRISHNA'S HELP

Shri Krishna, Balarama, Satyaki, Subhadra and the army of the Yadavas, along with Abhimanyu, came to Upaplavya from Dwarika. The King of Kashi, Shalya, Drupada, Dhrishtadyumna, Shikhandi, Draupadi's sons and many other kings came to the Matsya kingdom to attend the marriage of Abhimanyu. On the advice of Shri Krishna, a meeting of all the kings was convened. The kings declared that, as per the conditions laid down before the game of dice, the Pandavas had completed their twelve years in exile and had successfully lived incognito for one year. Hence, Dhritarashtra had to return their kingdom to them. The kings entrusted King Drupada with the responsibility of sending his able ambassador to Hastinapur in order to convince Dhritarashtra of this. There was also a possibility that Duryodhana might not agree to return their kingdom. It was thus decided that the Pandavas should begin preparations for a war. Shri Krishna, Balarama, Satyaki and others went back to Dwarika along with Abhimanyu and Uttara.

According to Shri Krishna's instructions, the Pandavas began preparations for the war. King Drupada and King Virata, along with their armies, had already come to support the Pandavas and to be by their side. Along with the huge armies of these kings, the Pandavas pitched their tents near Kurukshetra. Meanwhile, Duryodhana, too, had begun preparations for the war. Both the Kauravas and the Pandavas had begun to seek alliances with friendly kings and invited them to fight the war against the enemy. As a result, many kings and their armies started arriving in Kurukshetra. The Pandavas and the Kauravas had pitched their tents on the opposite sides of Kurukshetra.

Arjuna, on behalf of the Pandavas, went to Dwarika to seek Shri Krishna's help. Incidentally, Duryodhana also arrived there at the same time and for the same purpose. At that time, Shri Krishna was sleeping. So, Duryodhana sat beside Shri Krishna's head and waited for him to wake up. Arjuna stood near Shri Krishna's feet, waiting for him to wake up. After a while, when Shri Krishna woke up, he saw Arjuna standing at his feet. Shri Krishna said, "O Parth! When did you come here? What brings you here? I hope Yudhishthira and your other brothers are well."

Arjuna said, "O Keshava! I have come here to seek your help in the war."

An impatient Duryodhana immediately quipped, "Keshava! I came here first. Therefore, only I have the right to ask for your help first."

Shri Krishna said, "I love both of you equally. I will, without any prejudice or partiality, help both of you. If I will be with one of you, my Narayani army will be with the other side. I will neither hold any weapons in my hands nor take part in the war.

Since I saw Arjuna first, he has the right to ask for help first. And secondly, Arjuna being younger than you, courtesy demands that he should get a chance to select his option first."

Shri Krishna then asked Arjuna, "Parth! Tell me, whom do you choose?"

Arjuna replied, "O Keshava! I want you to be on our side. We need you, not your army."

Duryodhana was mighty pleased to hear these words of Arjuna. He only wanted Shri Krishna's army because the soldiers of the Narayani army were considered to be valiant and invincible. Duryodhana thanked Shri Krishna and then went to meet Balarama to seek his blessings. Having gained the Narayani army and the blessings of Balarama, an overjoyed Duryodhana returned to Hastinapur.

After Duryodhana had left, Shri Krishna asked Arjuna, "O Parth! I gave you a chance to choose first. Yet, why did you opt for me instead of my gallant army?"

Arjuna replied, "With your co-operation and under your able guidance, we can face the biggest and the most gallant of the armies with confidence. I request you to be my charioteer and guide me. That is more than enough for us."

Shri Krishna was pleased with Arjuna's reply. Arjuna then sought his blessings and left Dwarika.

Meanwhile, the maternal uncle of the Pandavas, King Shalya of Madra, had already set off, along with his army, to join the Pandava camp. Duryodhana wanted to win King Shalya over to his side. Therefore, he made grand arrangements to welcome King Shalya at various places along the route. Pleased with Duryodhana's hospitality, King Shalya said to him, "I am happy with your hospitality and services. Tell me, what should I give you in return?"

Duryodhana was waiting for this opportunity. At once, he said to King Shalya, "Uncle! I wish that you, along with your army, should be on our side and help us fight this war against the Pandavas."

King Shalya now realized that he had committed a blunder. But he was bound by the promise given to Duryodhana. Hence, he had no choice but to accede to Duryodhana's request. When Yudhishthira came to know about this incident, he was greatly pained.

38. A DELUSIVE DESIRE FOR PEACE

The Pandavas summoned all the kings who were their allies to join their camp. Innumerable armies and weapons from all over the country and abroad reached Kurukshetra. The Pandavas had collected about seven divisions of the army, while the Kauravas had collected about eleven divisions. One army division consisted of 21,870 chariots, 21,870 elephants, 65,610 horsemen and 1,09,350 soldiers on foot. Every warrior was well-equipped with a variety of weapons and equipment.

King Drupada's ambassador reached Hastinapur. He presented himself in the court of Dhritarashtra and said, "As per the condition laid down before the game of dice, the Pandavas have completed their twelve years in exile and have also lived incognito for one year. If their kingdom is returned to them, they are ready to forget their sufferings. The Pandavas desire peace. They do not wish to wage a war because they believe that a war never results in anyone's well-being, but it only leads to total destruction."

Supporting the views of King Drupada's ambassador, Bhishma *pitamaha* said, "The Pandavas have gained the support of many kings. It is a matter of great pleasure to know that, in spite of being well-prepared, they still wish to avert a war. Their demands are justified. Their kingdom must be restored to them."

An agitated Karna said to the ambassador, "Yudhishthira lost his kingdom in the game of dice. He has no right to demand the restoration of the kingdom. As per the condition of the game of dice, the Pandavas had to live in exile for twelve years and then live incognito for one year. But they have failed to fulfil this condition. Hence, they have to live in exile for another twelve years and then live incognito for one more year. Go and tell Yudhishthira that with the support of Drupada and Virata, he simply cannot frighten Duryodhana with his threats."

Dhritarashtra asked Karna to calm down. He then said to the ambassador, "Go and tell Yudhishthira that, within a few days, I will send my trusted minister Sanjaya with my message."

After some days, Sanjaya, Dhritarashtra's ambassador, came to Upaplavya to meet Yudhishthira. He said to the Pandavas, "Dhritarashtra sends his blessings to you all. He does not want a war. He, too, desires good-will and peace. But, Duryodhana and his friends are deceitful and scheming. In spite of Dhritarashtra and Bhishma *pitamaha's* appeals, they have refused to restore your kingdom. But you must be patient and not lose hope and courage."

Yudhishthira said to Sanjaya, "It is nice to know that uncle desires peace. But for the sake of peace, does he wish to put a begging bowl in our hands? Justice demands that we must get what actually belongs to us! We are five brothers. We will be happy and satisfied even if they give us Avisthala, Vrikasthala, Makandi, Varanavata and any one of the other towns. If they can fulfil this small demand of ours, a war will be averted."

Sanjaya returned to Hastinapur and conveyed Yudhishthira's message to Dhritarashtra. Bhishma *pitamaha* and Vidura fervently appealed to Dhritarashtra to make peace with the Pandavas. They also enlightened him about the divine powers of Shri Krishna and Arjuna. A boastful Karna threatened to kill Arjuna. When Bhishma *pitamaha* and Dronacharya warned Dhritarashtra about the dire consequences of the war, Dhritarashtra began to wail. Duryodhana said to him, "We have, on our side, gallant warriors and eleven divisions of army. Therefore, we can definitely defeat the Pandavas in this war. Please do not worry about anything."

Dhritarashtra's blind love for Duryodhana made him helpless before his son's stubborn attitude. He said to Bhishma *pitamaha*, Dronacharya and Vidura, "Duryodhana does not heed my advice. His decision will be the final decision now."

39. SHRI KRISHNA, THE AMBASSADOR OF PEACE

Ultimately, Duryodhana declared his decision to fight a war against the Pandavas.

After Dhritarashtra's ambassador Sanjaya left Upaplavya, Shri Krishna decided to go to Hastinapur and make a last-ditch effort for a peaceful settlement. Yudhishthira said to Shri Krishna, "I know that Duryodhana is very stubborn and that he will never give in. Hence, I do not think that you should go among those evil men and put your life in danger."

Shri Krishna said to Yudhishthira, "I am aware of the evil designs of Duryodhana. Yet we should make the last attempt to reach some sort of a peaceful settlement. If we fail to explore every possibility of averting a war, the world will never forgive us. I am going there as an ambassador of peace. If they try to misbehave with me or insult me, I can handle them. So, please do not worry about me."

Shri Krishna went to Hastinapur with Satyaki. There was joy and merriment all over the kingdom. The people of Hastinapur accorded a grand welcome to Shri Krishna. King Dhritarashtra, along with Duryodhana and Dusshasana, went to receive Shri Krishna at the gates of the city. Shri Krishna stayed with Vidura for the night. He met Kunti, his paternal aunt, and assured her of the well-being of the Pandavas. He said to her, "Sage Durvasa had given you a divine *mantra* to invoke Lord Surya, the Sun-god, who blessed you with a son – Karna. Now the time has come to tell Karna that he is your son. You must reveal to Karna his true identity and persuade him to fight on the side of the Pandavas against the Kauravas."

The following morning, Duryodhana and Shakuni came to Vidura's house to escort Shri Krishna to the court. In the court, Shri Krishna tried his best to convince Duryodhana to agree to the Pandavas' modest demand. He said to Duryodhana, "The Pandavas will be happy and satisfied with the five towns demanded by them."

A haughty Duryodhana said to Shri Krishna, "Five towns! As long as I am alive, I will not give even an inch of this land to the Pandavas."

Later, Bhishma *pitamaha*, Dhritarashtra and Gandhari also tried to persuade Duryodhana to agree to a peaceful settlement, but it was all in vain. Duryodhana refused to heed their advice. He insulted Shri Krishna and left the court. With the help of Karna, Dusshasana and Shakuni, he hatched a plot to imprison Shri Krishna. Satyaki warned Shri Krishna about Duryodhana's evil designs. It was then that Shri Krishna assumed his cosmic form and stunned the assembly. Even the blind Dhritarashtra got a glimpse of Shri Krishna's cosmic form. Shri Krishna said to Dhritarashtra, "O King Dhritarashtra! Duryodhana is a short-sighted fool. He thinks that he can easily imprison me. But he is not aware of the fact that, in a moment, I can destroy the whole Kaurava dynasty and crown Yudhishthira the King of Hastinapur even without fighting a war."

Shri Krishna's words frightened Dhritarashtra. Shri Krishna, along with Satyaki and Vidura, left the court and went to Vidura's house. He narrated the whole incident to Kunti. Kunti said, "Tell the Pandavas that the time has come for them to fulfil their duties as Kshatriyas. They will be victorious in the war. My blessings are with them. O Govind! Protect them during the war."

40. KUNTI MEETS KARNA

Shri Krishna had advised Kunti to meet Karna and reveal his true identity to him. Accordingly, early one morning, Kunti went to the banks of the river Ganga to meet Karna. Karna was worshipping the Sun-god at that time.

As the sun started moving up in the sky, Karna opened his eyes. He was surprised to see Kunti standing before him. He bowed to Kunti and said, "O Queen! Karna, the son of Adhiratha and Radha, bows to you in reverence. Tell me, what can I do for you?"

Kunti was impressed by Karna's conduct and cultured manners. She lovingly said, "Karna! You are not Adhiratha's son. In fact, you are my son. When I was with King Kuntibhoja, you were born to me before my marriage as a result of a boon granted to me by Surya, the Sun-god. You are the eldest brother of the Pandavas. Hence, I request you to join the Pandavas. I wish to see you and Arjuna together."

Karna said, "O Mother! It is impossible for me to join my brothers now. I am indebted to Duryodhana. He has supported me all my life. Today, he needs me more than anyone else. If I betray him in his hour of need, it will be an act of cowardice and selfishness on my part. You have lost the right to call me your son because you abandoned me soon after I was born. Yet you will not return empty-handed from here. I promise you that, among your five sons, I will kill only Arjuna. Thus, even after the war ends, you will still have five of your sons alive. You will have to lose one of your sons—either Karna or Arjuna."

Kunti blessed Karna and, with a heavy heart, she took her leave of him. However, Kunti was relieved that Karna had promised her that, except Arjuna, he would not kill any of the other brothers. Kunti was confident that no one could kill Arjuna because his charioteer was none other than Shri Krishna himself. Yet, being a mother, Kunti was terrified even with the thought of Karna's death during the war.

Meanwhile, Shri Krishna reached Upaplavya and told the Pandavas about his visit to Hastinapur and his endeavours for a peaceful settlement with the Kauravas. He then instructed and advised the Pandavas to fully prepare themselves for the war by resorting to the four expedients of diplomacy : *Sama, Dama, Danda* and *Bheda* : the policy of conciliation, money, punishment and split.

41. PREPARATIONS FOR THE WAR AND THE TEACHINGS OF THE GEETA

According to Shri Krishna's advice and instructions, the Pandavas began their preparations for the war. They appointed seven commanders—Drupada, Virata, Dhrishtadyumna, Shikhandi, Satyaki, Chekitana and Bheema for the seven divisions of their army. Dhrishtadyumna was also appointed as the Commander-in-Chief of the whole Pandava army.

The Kauravas had eleven divisions of the army. They also had valiant warriors like Bhishma, Drona, Karna, Kripacharya, Shalya, Ashwatthama, Jayadratha, Kritavarma, Bhoorishrava and Bhagadatta. Bhishma *pitamaha* was the Commander-in-Chief of the Kaurava army. Bhishma said to Duryodhana, "I will destroy the Pandava army, but I refuse to kill the Pandavas."

Karna said to Duryodhana, "As long as Bhishma *pitamaha* is present on the battlefield, I will not fight this war."

Duryodhana had to accept the conditions laid down by Bhishma *pitamaha* and Karna because he needed their co-operation, help and support in the war.

At that time, Sage Vyasa came to meet Dhritarashtra. Dhritarashtra bowed to him and said, "Being blind, I will not be able to watch the war. However, I wish to get all the news of each and every moment of the war."

Sage Vyasa said, "I will bless your trusted minister Sanjaya with divine vision. Sitting here with you, he will be able to watch the war and describe it to you in detail."

Saying this, Sage Vyasa gifted Sanjaya with the divine vision and left.

After the preparations and the necessary arrangements for the war were completed, the armies of the Kauravas and the Pandavas came to Kurukshetra and stood on the opposite sides. Shri Krishna blew his conch, the *Panchajanya*. Hearing the sound of Shri Krishna's conch, the commanders of the Kaurava army also blew their conches.

173

The Commanders-in-Chief of both the armies met each other and decided the rules and principles of the war :

(1) The fighting will be stopped for the day at sunset every day.

(2) Neither will attack the injured, the unsuspecting and the soldier who is either unarmed or is fleeing the battlefield.

(3) Every warrior will fight only against his equal in the enemy camp. A warrior in a chariot will only fight against his enemy warrior in a chariot. Similarly, soldiers on horseback or on foot will fight only against their counterparts in the enemy camp.

(4) When two warriors are fighting against each other, no other warrior will interfere or intervene.

These rules were decided upon by mutual consent.

Bhishma *pitamaha* exhorted his warriors to fight gallantly. His words of inspiration were welcomed by his army with loud blowing of bugles and conches. The thunderous cries 'May the Kauravas be victorious' permeated the battlefield and reached the skies. A flag depicting a coconut palm and five stars adorned Bhishma *pitamaha's* chariot.

Ashwatthama's flag had the picture of a lion, while Dronacharya's flag bore the picture of a *kamandal* and a bow and an arrow. Duryodhana's flag had the *Sheshanaga*, Kripacharya's flag depicted *Nandi*, the holy bull and Jayadratha's flag bore the symbols of bears. The whole battlefield of Kurukshetra was adorned with colourful flags depicting a variety of symbols.

On hearing the loud war cries of the Kauravas, Bheema became alert. The army of the Pandavas was smaller compared to that of the Kauravas, and so Bheema had arranged his army in the shape of a needle.

Bhishma *pitamaha* led the army of the Kauravas, while that of the Pandavas was led by Arjuna in his chariot, the *Nandighosh*. Shri Krishna was Arjuna's charioteer. When Arjuna saw his elders, cousins and his near and dear ones standing before him, ready to fight against him, he thought, "What is the use of that kingdom which will be acquired by killing my own brothers, near and dear ones, elders and *gurus* ? Thousands of women will be widowed and innumerable children will be orphaned at the end of this war."

Thinking thus, Arjuna said to Shri Krishna, "O Keshava! It is immoral and unethical to fight the war in which you have to kill your own people. I am terrified and I have lost courage at the very thought of the dire consequences of this war. I cannot hold the *gandeev* in my hands. I will not be able to fight this war."

Shri Krishna realized that Arjuna's love for his elders, relatives, near and dear ones had made him lose sight of his goal. He could no longer differentiate between the right and the wrong. As a result, was under the impression that it was he alone who was doing all that. This had given rise to a feeling of false pride in Arjuna. Shri Krishna preached the teachings of the Geeta to Arjuna in order to enlighten him about the truth.*

Shri Krishna explained to Arjuna, "You are not going to kill even one of those people. They are all destined to die and you will be only instrumental in their doom. You have to fulfil your duty as a Kshatriya. The soul is immortal. It is of no use grieving for it. Man must perform his duty without worrying about the reward."

Having said this, Shri Krishna gave Arjuna the glimpse of his cosmic form. Arjuna saw that the whole Kaurava army was being absorbed into Shri Krishna's mouth, just like offerings into the sacrificial fire. Having understood and realized his duty to fight the war, Arjuna picked up his *gandeev* and got ready for the war.

Yudhishthira got down from his chariot and went to Bhishma *pitamaha* to seek his blessings. Bhishma *pitamaha* said, "I am bound by my vow to be on the side of the Kauravas during this war. But Arjuna is more valiant than I am. When the time comes, he will surely defeat me in this war."

Yudhishthira then took the blessings of Dronacharya and Kripacharya. They blessed him to be victorious in the war. Seeing the dignity and courtesy of Yudhishthira, Yuyutsu's (Duryodhana's stepbrother) eyes were filled with tears. He ran to embrace Yudhishthira. Yudhishthira blessed Yuyutsu, who then returned and took his place in the Kaurava army.

---

* The important *shlokas* from the Geeta are given in the appendix.

42. THE WAR BEGINS

After seeking the blessings of Bhishma, Drona and Kripacharya, Yudhishthira returned to the Pandavas' side and sat in his chariot. The chariot of Bhishma *pitamaha*, the oldest and the most gallant commander of the Kaurava army, stood before that of Dhrishtadyumna, the young and efficient Commander-in-Chief of the Pandava army. Arjuna and Shri Krishna blew their conches, the *Devadatta* and the *Panchajanya,* respectively. A fierce battle began. Abhimanyu was fighting bravely, showering a volley of arrows at the enemy. Arjuna, Bheema and Dhrishtadyumna resisted Bhishma's attacks with all their might. Throughout the day, both the Kauravas and the Pandavas fought intensely with all their might and courage. The fighting was stopped for the day at sunset. On this first day, the Pandavas lost their innumerable soldiers. Cheering up a distraught Yudhishthira, Shri Krishna said, "O Dharmaraja! Do not grieve. Ultimately, the truth will triumph and everything will come to a pleasant and happy ending."

The Pandavas knew that as long as Bhishma was alive, it would be difficult to defeat the Kauravas. Arjuna loved and revered Bhishma so much that he did not have the heart to kill him. Bhishma was a strong and brave warrior. As a boon, he was granted the power to die at will. Every day, Arjuna would make up his mind to kill Bhishma, but he would change his mind at the last moment. In this way, passed five days of the war.

It was the dawn of the sixth day of the war. Bheema, Ghatotkacha and Abhimanyu terrorized the Kaurava army by attacking it fiercely. Duryodhana was enraged at this. In spite of having brave warriors like Bhishma, Drona and Kripacharya, his army was being destroyed! Duryodhana said to Bhishma, "You have always immensely loved the Pandavas. That is the reason why you do not wish to defeat them."

Bhishma replied, "The Pandavas are the sons of Pandu, my nephew. Hence, there is nothing wrong if I love them. But you also seem to forget the fact that they can win because they are honest, virtuous and righteous. Yet I am doing my duty by fighting this war on your side. Tomorrow I will use the *Narayanastra* against the Pandavas."

At that point of time, only Bhishma had the *Narayanastra*. It was an extremely powerful weapon. When released, the *Narayanastra* killed all those who came within its radius. The following day, as promised, Bhishma released the *Narayanastra* at the Pandava army. Shri Krishna immediately asked all his soldiers to put their weapons down on the ground. He knew that the *Narayanastra* could not kill the unarmed. As instructed by Shri Krishna, all the soldiers of the Pandava army put down their weapons. But, Bheema was so engrossed in fighting that he did not hear Shri Krishna's instruction. He still had his weapon in his hands. Shri Krishna rushed towards Bheema and stood in front of him.

He absorbed the destructive power of the *Narayanastra* into his own body. Being an incarnation of *Narayana*, Shri Krishna was not at all affected by the *Narayanastra*. The destructive power of the *Narayanastra* safely passed through the body of Shri Krishna and thus the Pandava army was saved from a major destruction.

43. BHISHMA IS INJURED

The fierce war between the Kauravas and the Pandavas continued. Soon the war entered the ninth day. Both the camps had lost innumerable brave warriors. But, Bhishma was still as firm and determined as ever. The soldiers of both the armies were desperate to eliminate one another. Sometimes it appeared that the Pandavas would win the war; but suddenly the balance would tilt and then the Kauravas would prove to be stronger than the Pandavas. King Virata's two sons, Uttar and Shwet had laid down their lives in this war. The Pandavas were shocked at their deaths.

Shri Krishna asked Arjuna, "Parth! Why don't you kill Bhishma? Unless Bhishma is killed, this war will never end. If you do not kill him, I will have to take up that responsibility."

Saying this, Shri Krishna got down from his chariot and rushed towards Bhishma's chariot. But Arjuna followed him and pleaded with him to stop. He said, "Please do not break your vow. I will surely kill Bhishma tomorrow."

At dawn, on the tenth day, the war began. According to Shri Krishna's instructions, Dhrishtadyumna asked Shikhandi to be Arjuna's charioteer. Shikhandi was actually King Drupada's daughter. She performed harsh penance to transform herself into a man. Besides, in her previous birth, she was born as Amba, the daughter of the King of Kashi. Bhishma had abducted her, only to abandon her later on. So she had vowed to punish Bhishma and then killed herself. As soon as Bhishma saw Shikhandi coming towards him, he immediately laid down his weapons. He said, "Shikhandi was born as a female. Therefore I cannot use my weapons against him."

Bhishma now knew that his end was near. He quietly prepared himself for his own death.

Arjuna had also decided to kill Bhishma that day. He aimed and shot innumerable arrows from his *gandeev* at Bhishma. The arrows pierced Bhishma's body. Bhishma bravely endured the relentless attack of Arjuna's arrows. He said to himself, "These are the arrows of my grandson Arjuna. Only Arjuna can kill me."

Arjuna's arrows pierced Bhishma's body right from the neck up to the legs. At last, a seriously wounded Bhishma fell down from his chariot. But, because of the innumerable arrows pierced in his body, the body remained above the ground. The arrows supported his body like a bed, but only his head was hanging loose without any support. He screamed, "Somebody please support my head."

The soldiers of both the armies stopped fighting and surrounded Bhishma. One of them said, "Go and bring a pillow befitting a gallant warrior."

Some of the soldiers rushed to get a pillow. But only Arjuna knew what kind of a pillow his grandfather was yearning for. He quickly shot three arrows exactly under Bhishma's head. The arrows struck the ground and gave the much needed support to Bhishma *pitamaha's* head. Bhishma lay his head on the arrows and an expression of great pain crossed his face. Duryodhana came running to where Bhishma lay. He thought that the Kauravas would now surely be defeated. Bhishma said, "Duryodhana! You still have a chance for a settlement with the Pandavas. It is not too late. You must restore their kingdom to them."

Duryodhana ignored the words of this great man. He quietly left the place. After a while, Bhishma requested Arjuna, "I am thirsty. Arjuna! Get me some water to drink."

Arjuna shot an arrow into the ground right next to the spot where Bhishma lay. A fountain of pure water gushed out of the earth and started falling into Bhishma's mouth. Everybody standing there said, "This is the water of the river Ganga. The goddess Ganga herself has come to quench the thirst of her son Gangeya."

After quenching his thirst, Bhishma said to the Kauravas and the Pandavas, "Lying here, I will keep an eye on all of you. I will witness this war. I will breathe my last on the day when the sun enters the Tropic of Cancer."

Thousands of soldiers crowded around Bhishma. Some stood in stoic silence, while the others wept bitterly. Shikhandi had helped the Pandavas to kill Bhishma. Hence, the boon granted to him by Lord Shiva had come true.

Karna rushed to Bhishma and fell at his feet. Breaking down, he said, "*Pitamaha*! My hatred and anger for you have always compelled me to behave rudely and in a very harsh manner with you. Please forgive me for my misconduct."

Bhishma replied, "I always knew that you are Kunti's son and so I loved you as much as I loved the Pandavas. But I had promised myself that I would never tell this secret to anyone. O Karna! Now you must try for a settlement between the Kauravas and the Pandavas. You are the elder brother of the Pandavas. Please do not fight against your own brothers."

Karna argued, "I cannot do that now. I have vowed to help Duryodhana and kill Arjuna."

"In that case, you do your duty," said Bhishma.

Saying this, Bhishma blessed Karna. Duryodhana asked Karna to take over as the Commander-in-Chief of the Kaurava army. But Karna argued that Drona was more suitable for the job. Hence, Duryodhana requested Dronacharya to assume the responsibilities as the Commander-in-Chief of the Kaurava army.

Duryodhana said to Dronacharya, "I want you to capture Yudhishthira alive so that we can end the war."

Duryodhana thought, "If I capture Yudhishthira alive, the war will obviously come to an end. Then, once again, I will defeat them in a game of dice. Defeating the Pandavas in a game of dice is easier than defeating them in a war."

Dronacharya, however, was glad to know that Duryodhana wished to keep Yudhishthira alive. Drona, too, loved the Pandavas very much. The Pandavas were his favourite pupils and so he did not wish to kill them.

On the eleventh and the twelfth day of the war, Dronacharya tried his best to capture Yudhishthira alive. But he could not succeed in his endeavours because Yudhishthira was always accompanied by Arjuna along with his strongest weapon, the *gandeev*. At last, Dronacharya said to Duryodhana, "I can capture Yudhishthira only if Arjuna is kept away from him."

44. THE DEATH OF ABHIMANYU

On the thirteenth day of the war, King Susharma of Trigarta challenged Arjuna to fight against him. As they were fighting against each other, Susharma took Arjuna far away from the battlefield. Arjuna put Dhrishtadyumna, Bheema and Satyaki in charge of Yudhishthira's security and went to fight against Susharma.

Taking advantage of this opportunity, Dronacharya formed the *Chakravyuha*. King Jayadratha of Sindhu said to him, "Lord Shiva has granted me the boon that none of the Pandavas, except Arjuna, can defeat me in a war. Therefore, I will stand at the entrance to the *Chakravyuha* and prevent the Pandavas from entering it."

Among the Pandavas, only Arjuna knew how to break through the *Chakravyuha*. Abhimanyu had some knowledge about the *Chakravyuha*. Yudhishthira called him and said, "Since only you have some knowledge about the *Chakravyuha*, help us to break through it."

Abhimanyu, the son of Arjuna and Subhadra, was a descendant of Varcha, the son of a *Vasu* called Soma. Arjuna had made him proficient in ten branches of knowledge and had also taught him the use of divine weapons. Impressed with his skills in the use of arms, his maternal uncle Balarama had given him his bow called the *Raudra*. Abhimanyu was married to Balarama's daughter Vatsala and King Virata's daughter Uttara.

Abhimanyu's chariot was a grand one. It was pulled by black and yellow horses with grey eyes. The reins of the horses were in the hands of Sumitra, an able charioteer.

Abhimanyu was a valiant and an adventurous warrior like his father Arjuna and his maternal uncle Shri Krishna. He knew how to break through the *Chakravyuha*, but he did not know how to come out of it. Yet he took up the responsibility of entering the *Chakravyuha*. He said to Bheema, "In the *Chakravyuha*, the army of the Kauravas will be arranged in the form of a lotus. There will be seven arrays with seven doors, each door protected by a guard. Each guard will be aided by a huge well-armed army.

I will break through all the seven arrays and enter the *Chakravyuha*. But I do not know how to come out of it. Only if all the elders remain with me and support me, will I be able to break through the *Chakravyuha* and come out of it safely."

Bheema assured Abhimanyu, "Son, do not worry. All of us will follow you closely and remain with you constantly. Hence, once you enter the *Chakravyuha*, we will help you to come out of it."

Abhimanyu said to Bheema, "Uncle! In that case, I will surely succeed in routing the enemy today."

Yudhishthira was delighted to see young Abhimanyu's confidence and spirit of adventure. He lovingly embraced him and blessed him saying, "Son! May you be victorious in today's war."

Yudhishthira crowned Abhimanyu the Commander-in-Chief of the Pandava army. Abhimanyu sought the blessings of Yudhishthira and Bheema and asked his charioteer Sumitra to drive the chariot towards the door of the *Chakravyuha*. Yudhishthira, Bheema, Nakula, Sahadeva, Dhrishtadyumna, Satyaki and others immediately followed Abhimanyu.

Abhimanyu's charioteer drove the chariot in such a brilliant way that Dronacharya, who was standing at the first door of the *Chakravyuha*, could not stop him. Abhimanyu, Bheema and the other soldiers entered the *Chakravyuha*. The huge army of the Kauravas rushed forward to stop them. A fierce battle ensued between the two armies. The valiant Abhimanyu killed innumerable soldiers of the Kaurava army. He was killing the enemies by thousands. It seemed as though he was Death itself. Even some of the great warriors were so frightened by Abhimanyu's onslaught that they struggled to save their lives.

Dronacharya was watching Abhimanyu's skills in the war. Accompanied by some warriors, a worried Dronacharya went to fight against Abhimanyu.

King Ashmaka, who accompanied Dronacharya, was killed by Abhimanyu. King Shalya, who could not bear the attack of Abhimanyu, fell down unconscious. King Shalya's brother rushed there with a huge army. But within a few moments, they, too, were killed by Abhimanyu. Even the gallant Karna could not withstand the fierce attack of Abhimanyu.

Abhimanyu was so busy fighting against the Kaurava army, that he left Bheema and the others far behind him. Along the way into the *Chakravyuha*, Abhimanyu was continuing his work of destroying the Kaurava army. Dronacharya praised the skills of Abhimanyu. Thus, an angry Dusshasana attacked Abhimanyu. With a fierce shower of arrows, Abhimanyu wounded Dusshasana. Thinking that Dusshasana was dead, his charioteer took him away from the battlefield.

Seeing the pitiable condition of Dusshasana, Karna and his brother Radheya came forward to fight with Abhimanyu. But, Abhimanyu defeated Karna and killed his brother Radheya.

Abhimanyu could not see Bheema and the other Pandava soldiers. On his way into the *Chakravyuha*, he had killed thousands of enemy soldiers and so he presumed that Bheema and his army would easily come to his help.

Abhimanyu could have been right. But, Jayadratha had stopped Bheema and the other warriors. Lord Shiva had granted Jayadratha the boon that none of the Pandavas, except Arjuna, could defeat him in a war. Hence, Jayadratha was successful in keeping the Pandavas from following Abhimanyu. Therefore, in spite of all their efforts, Bheema, Nakula, Sahadeva, Dhrishtadyumna, Satyaki and the other warriors could not go to Abhimanyu's help.

While Abhimanyu was waiting for Bheema and the other warriors, Karna's son Vrishasena rushed forward to attack him. Great warriors like Satyashrava, Shalya's son Rukmaratha and his hundred brothers, Duryodhana's son Lakshmana and King Kratha were protecting Vrishasena. In the presence of all these gallant warriors, Abhimanyu killed him. Hence, Dronacharya, Karna, Kripacharya, Ashwatthama, Kritvarma and Brihadbala, the six great warriors, attacked Abhimanyu with a shower of arrows. But the brave Abhimanyu harassed them, too. He killed ten thousand warriors including King Brihadbala.

Trembling with fear, Karna said to Dronacharya, "*Acharya*! There is no way we can save ourselves from the deadly onslaught of Abhimanyu."

Dronacharya assigned a job to each of the warriors including Karna. He then broke Abhimanyu's armour and killed his horses. At the same time, when Dronacharya signalled to him, Karna broke Abhimanyu's bow. Meanwhile, Kritvarma killed his charioteer.

Taking his sword and shield, Abhimanyu jumped out of his chariot. Dronacharya then broke the sword and Karna broke the shield. At last, Abhimanyu took a wheel of his chariot in his hands and started whirling it about his head. At that time, Dronacharya shot an arrow and broke the wheel, too. A furious Abhimanyu then took up the mace and killed Ashwatthama's charioteer, the horses of his chariot and many soldiers.

It appeared as though Abhimanyu was Death itself. There was no stopping to his fierce onslaught. There were heaps and heaps of dead bodies all over the battlefield. Suddenly Dusshasana's son hit him with a mace. Abhimanyu fell down. But, he soon recovered. He was just about to rise when he was again hit on the head by a mace. Abhimanyu fell down, never to rise again.

Jayadratha ran to the seriously wounded Abhimanyu and kicked him on his head. Meanwhile, Dronacharya, Karna, Dusshasana, Duryodhana, Ashwatthama and others came to Abhimanyu, who was breathing his last. Abhimanyu addressed them saying, "Having fought bravely in this war, I do not regret that I will breathe my last here after falling down wounded. But I certainly feel bad about the fact that even after I fell down, Jayadratha insulted me by kicking me on my head."

Dronacharya felt sorry for Abhimanyu. He was pained to hear his words. After some time, Abhimanyu died.

In the evening, when Arjuna returned to the Pandava camp after defeating Susharma and his soldiers, an eerie silence greeted him. Arjuna could sense an intuitive apprehension of some grave misfortune. When he was told about Abhimanyu's untimely death, he began to wail. Shri Krishna tried to console Yudhishthira and Arjuna. At that moment, somebody came and told them that before breathing his last Abhimanyu had said, "I feel bad about the fact that even after I fell down, Jayadratha insulted me by kicking me on my head."

Arjuna was also informed that Jayadratha had prevented Bheema and the other Pandava soldiers from entering the *Chakravyuha* to help Abhimanyu.

Arjuna solemnly vowed,

"I will kill Jayadratha before sunset tomorrow. If I fail to fulfil my vow, I will immolate myself by entering fire."

45. THE SLAYING OF JAYADRATHA AND DRONACHARYA'S DEATH

Early next morning, Arjuna mounted his chariot. He had spent the previous night mourning the death of Abhimanyu. The very thoughts of avenging his beloved son's death by killing Jayadratha had kept him alive. Arjuna had vowed to kill Jayadratha before sunset that day.

Duryodhana's spies warned him about Arjuna's vow. When King Jayadratha heard about Arjuna's solemn vow, he began to tremble with fear. He was not even ready to enter the battlefield. Duryodhana said to him, "Have no fear, my friend. We are all with you. We will remain with you and protect you from Arjuna."

Having been assured of full security by Duryodhana, Jayadratha was now prepared to enter the battlefield. When the battle began that day, Jayadratha was being protected by Dronacharya, Ashwatthama, Karna, Duryodhana and many other warriors. Arjuna began to fight against Drona first. But, Dronacharya did not give in easily.

The sun was about to set. Arjuna had not yet succeeded in fulfilling his vow. It was then that Shri Krishna, for some time, covered the sun with clouds and fog. Jayadratha and the Kauravas thought that the sun had set and it was time to stop the fighting for the day. They thought, "The sun has set and hence, Jayadratha does not face any danger from Arjuna." But, Arjuna kept on fighting. Dronacharya had given Duryodhana an impenetrable armour. No arrows could ever pierce it. Therefore, Arjuna shot innumerable arrows at those parts of Duryodhana's body which were not covered by that armour. A wounded Duryodhana had to leave the battlefield.

Jayadratha now believed that there was no danger to his life from Arjuna and so he became incautious. Taking advantage of Jayadratha's imprudence, Arjuna showered a volley of arrows at his head. Jayadratha's head was severed from his body and thus, Arjuna succeeded in fulfilling his vow.

That day, the Kauravas and the Pandavas fought against one another with a mad rage. Dronacharya fought against Bheema, while Karna fought against Nakula and Bheema. Bheema killed several brothers of Duryodhana. Karna would have killed Bheema, but he had promised Kunti that, except Arjuna, he would not kill any of the Pandavas. Thus Bheema's life was saved.

There was a fierce battle between Karna and Bheema's son Ghatotkacha. Ghatotkacha harassed Karna with his illusory powers. Karna was not able to withstand Ghatotkacha's attacks and so he found it extremely difficult to defeat him. Exasperated with this utter confusion, Karna used the *Amogha Shakti* given to him by Lord Indra to kill Ghatotkacha. It was only after Ghatotkacha's death that Karna realized that he had to use the *Amogha Shakti* only to kill Arjuna. After taking the life of Ghatotkacha, Karna lost the *Amogha Shakti*. He stood there helpless and defenceless while he saw the *Amogha Shakti* going back to Lord Indra. Now he had to fight against Arjuna without that divine weapon. Karna now regretted his blunder.

Shri Krishna removed the cover of the clouds and fog which had so far concealed the sun. The sun shone brightly for some time in the clear sky. But soon, the sun set and it grew dark. However, Duryodhana ordered his army to continue fighting. The war continued throughout the night, during which Bheema killed all the Kauravas, except Duryodhana and Dusshasana. He was shocked at the death of his son Ghatotkacha, but Yudhishthira calmed him down by consoling him.

Karna and Dronacharya were fighting with great passion. The Pandavas realized that it was time to eliminate Dronacharya. They began to think of a plan to kill him. Shri Krishna said to them, "Let the words 'Ashwatthama is dead' fill the atmosphere. When Dronacharya hears these loud shouts, he will think that his son is dead and so he will lay down his weapons and leave the battlefield. You can easily kill him then."

Expressing his displeasure, Yudhishthira argued, "Keshava! You are asking us to tell a blatant lie! No. Never! I will never be able to tell a lie."

At that very moment, Bheema wielded his mace and killed an elephant called Ashwatthama. Then he cried out loudly, "I have killed Ashwatthama. Ashwatthama is dead."

Dronacharya was alarmed to hear these words.

"This cannot be true," he cried, "This can never be true. Ashwatthama is not killed. Ashwatthama cannot die because he is blessed with immortality."

Saying this, Dronacharya started walking towards Yudhishthira to confirm the news. Dronacharya was sure that Yudhishthira would never tell a lie. He asked him in a loud voice, "Yudhishthira! Is it true that Ashwatthama has been killed?"

Poor Yudhishthira! He stood there stunned and pained. His soldiers stared at his face, trying to read his expressions. If Yudhishthira spoke the truth, he would have to lose the war. Unable to take a quick decision, Yudhishthira closed his eyes and thought, "I will have to tell a lie in order to save the lives of my soldiers. I have no choice but to commit this sin today." Having made up his mind, Yudhishthira said in a loud voice, "Gurudev! It is true that Ashwatthama has been killed."

"नरो वा कुञ्जरो वा।, the man or the elephant," he immediately muttered.

As expected, no one could hear the words muttered by Yudhishthira. Dronacharya began to wail loudly. He laid down his weapons and sat down on the ground, dejected and disconsolate. Ashwatthama was a gallant warrior and Dronacharya loved him more than his own life.

Ashwatthama was immortal. Hence, Dronacharya had dreamt that, after all the brave warriors were killed in the war, Ashwatthama would be the only one to survive and that ultimately, he would rule over the whole world. But now that Ashwatthama was no more, for whom should Dronacharya fight the war?

Yudhishthira had never told a lie before. Even the gods respected him for his love for truth and justice. But that day, for the first time in his life, Yudhishthira had told a lie. As a result, his chariot which usually moved about four inches above the ground, instantly came down with a thud. Now, like the chariots of other ordinary men, his chariot, too, moved on the ground.

Hearing the news of Ashwatthama's death, Dronacharya had already laid down his weapons because he did not wish to fight the war any more. He sat in meditation and started praying. At that time, Dhrishtadyumna rushed towards him. All the soldiers standing there tried to prevent him from attacking Dronacharya. But with one stroke of his sword, Dhrishtadyumna severed Dronacharya's head from his body. Everybody was stunned by this brutal act of Dhrishtadyumna.

According to the rules of the war, it was immoral and unethical to slay an unarmed warrior. Besides, it was a sin to kill any man who was meditating or saying his prayers. But such a sin and an unethical act had become necessary to eliminate Dronacharya. Many years ago, with the help of the princes of Hastinapur, Dronacharya had captured and insulted Drupada. With a view to avenging that insult, Drupada had fasted, meditated and performed harsh penance to invoke the gods. The gods had, according to Drupada's wishes, blessed him with a son who would ultimately kill Dronacharya. Drupada's son Dhrishtadyumna had now killed Dronacharya, who, once upon a time, had been Drupada's dear friend.

46. THE DEATH OF KARNA

After Dronacharya's death, Karna was appointed the Commander-in-Chief of the Kaurava army. Duryodhana was deeply shocked at the death of Drona. Ashwatthama fought even more fiercely in order to avenge his father's death. He showered fiery arrows at the Pandava army. The Pandavas could not protect themselves from the attack of Ashwatthama's arrows.

Meanwhile, Bheema challenged Dusshasana to a duel. It was Dusshasana who had dishonoured Draupadi in the court of Hastinapur. At that time, Bheema had vowed : "I will sever the dirty hands with which Dusshasana has dared to touch Draupadi's hair and I will also tear open Dusshasana's chest and drink his blood." Bheema broke Dusshasana's right hand and hurled it towards the sky. He then mercilessly tore open his chest and drank his blood. Thus, Bheema avenged Dusshasana's indecent behaviour with Draupadi in the court of Hastinapur and fulfilled his vows.

Karna fought against Nakula, Sahadeva and Yudhishthira. He got many opportunities to kill each of them, but he was bound by the promise given to Kunti. At last, Karna and Arjuna came face to face on the battlefield. King Shalya (Nakula and Sahadeva's maternal uncle) was Karna's charioteer.

The fight between Karna and Arjuna began. The soldiers stopped fighting to watch the two great warriors in action. They had just one baffling question in their minds : Who will be victorious? Karna had already lost the *Amogha Shakti* given to him by Lord Indra. Yet he appeared to be fighting against Arjuna with great skill and confidence. Arjuna, too, was equally proficient in facing Karna's aggression. After some time, one of the wheels of Karna's chariot got stuck in the ground. Karna struggled to lift it free and drive the chariot along, but he could not do so. Karna requested Arjuna to stop the fighting for some time so that he could get down and lift the wheel of the chariot. Arjuna was about to put down his bow, when Shri Krishna said to him, "You do not have to stop fighting, Parth! Karna has not only supported Duryodhana's misdeeds but he has also been a party to all his evil designs. Have you forgotten that seven warriors of the Kaurava army got together and killed an unarmed Abhimanyu. Karna never even thought about principles and ethics then. So, pick up your bow, aim an arrow and shoot to kill Karna."

Arjuna picked up his most powerful weapon, the *gandeev*, and aimed an arrow at Karna. With lightning speed, the arrow struck Karna and he dropped down dead. A sun-like brilliant flame emerged from Karna's body and went towards heaven. Arjuna failed to understand why his heart was filled with sadness and remorse at the death of Karna. His eyes were filled with tears. He said to himself, "This war is full of lies and brutality. Both the Kauravas and the Pandavas are fighting this war without following any ethical principles! This is the reason why thousands of innocent brave soldiers are killed in this war every day."

209

47. THE DEATH OF DURYODHANA

After Karna's death King Shalya was appointed the Commander-in-Chief of the Kaurava army. The soldiers of both the camps had been continuously fighting for seventeen days now. It was the eighteenth day of the war. Yudhishthira and Shalya prepared themselves well and stood face to face on the battlefield. A fierce fight ensued between the two. It was a fight to the finish situation for both. Finally, Yudhishthira killed Shalya. Nakula and Sahadeva killed Shakuni and his son.

Duryodhana was overcome with grief and shock. He had lost not only all his brothers but also his most loyal, trusted and beloved friend, Karna. Karna had always stood by him. A dejected and defeated Duryodhana walked towards a lake near Kurukshetra. He entered the lake and hid himself in the deep waters.

Yudhishthira had seen Duryodhana going towards the lake. Accompained by the Pandavas, he followed him to the lake and said loudly,

"O cruel Duryodhana! Come out of the water. Why are you hiding yourself?"

Duryodhana replied, "You can take the kingdom of Hastinapur. I do not want it now. I have lost all my brothers in this war. Therefore, I do not wish to live any more."

An angry Yudhishthira roared, "Ah! So now you are ready to restore my kingdom to me! We have already won our kingdom in this war. Your obstinacy has resulted in the loss of thousands of innocent lives. Therefore, I command you to come out of the water and fight against us like a true Kshatriya."

Duryodhana was alone against the five Pandavas. So, he refused to fight against them. Yudhishthira assured him, "According to the principles of war, only one of us will fight against you."

Relieved, Duryodhana came out of the water. He hated Bheema so much that he challenged him to a duel. Yudhishthira gave a mace to Duryodhana and the duel began. The duel continued for a very long time because both were equally strong. It was a very exciting and breath-taking duel. At last, Shri Krishna patted his thigh and gestured to Bheema to hit Duryodhana on the thigh.

In the court of Hastinapur, Duryodhana had gestured to Draupadi to sit on his thigh. At that time, Bheema had vowed to break Duryodhana's thigh with a blow of his mace. Bheema then remembered that vow. But hitting the opponent below the waist was against the rules of a duel. Bheema was puzzled. So, as soon as he got the opportunity, Bheema hurled his mace in the air.

At the same moment, Duryodhana jumped up high in the air. Bheema's mace hit Duryodhana so hard on his thigh that the thigh was smashed. A badly wounded Duryodhana fell down on the ground. Bheema kicked him and crushed his head under his feet. The rest of the Pandavas were horrified to see the scene. Yudhishthira angrily shouted, "Stop, Bheema! Your act does not befit a brave Kshatriya. After all, Duryodhana is our cousin."

Duryodhana said to Yudhishthira, "Let him do whatever he wants to do. Do not stop him. I do not care for anything now. You killed Karna and Drona by breaking the rules of war. You have won this war by resorting to unethical tactics. Now you may take this kingdom overflowing with dead bodies. For the rest of your lives, you will have to see the sad faces of thousands of widows and orphans. How will you enjoy and be happy in such a kingdom?"

On hearing these words, Yudhishthira hung his head in shame. The other brothers, too, were ashamed and sadly looked at one another's face. But Shri Krishna could not tolerate the verbal attack of Duryodhana. He took him to task and said, "Have you forgotten that, all your life, you have committed grave misdeeds and sins? You have always behaved in an unethical and immoral manner. You and your accomplices cheated Yudhishthira in the game of dice and dishonoured and insulted Draupadi. You did not leave any stone unturned to harass the Pandavas in exile. Without any reason, you waged a war against Virata and refused to restore the Pandavas' kingdom to them. Why didn't you think of ethics and morality when you killed an unarmed Abhimanyu? Today, when you are paying a heavy price for your dissatisfaction, jealousy, greed, misdeeds and sins, you should be ashamed even to think about ethics and morality. How dare you talk about ethics! You know that you have never done anything ethical or moral even for one single moment in your life."

Then addressing the Pandavas, Shri Krishna said, "If you had not resorted to unfair and unethical means, you could have never defeated Duryodhana in this war. Being your well-wisher, I had to use my illusory powers to help you win this war. There is no reason for you to feel guilty or regret your acts now. The sun will soon set. So, let us return to our camps."

After Shri Krishna and the Pandavas had left, Ashwatthama came to Duryodhana who was nearing his death and vowed to avenge his miserable condition. Duryodhana crowned him the Commander-in-Chief of the Kaurava army. Ashwatthama then returned to his camp.

That night, a depressed Ashwatthama was sitting in his tent. Suddenly, he spotted an owl which was killing some birds sleeping in the dark of the night. Seeing this, a cruel and an evil idea struck him. He got up and tiptoed in the dark of the night towards the Pandava camp and crept into one of the tents. He saw that Dhrishtadyumna and Draupadi's five sons were sleeping there peacefully. Their armours and weapons lay beside them. Taking advantage of the opportunity, Ashwatthama brutally killed them and having accomplished his task, he quietly returned to Duryodhana and gave him the news of the Pandava casualties. A delighted Duryodhana praised Ashwatthama saying, "You have accomplished a great task for me. Even the great warriors like Bhishma, Dronacharya and Karna could not achieve this for me. You are, indeed, an efficient commander." Saying this, Duryodhana breathed his last.

The following morning, Shri Krishna and the Pandavas were shocked and appalled to know about the brutal killings in their camp. A grief-stricken Draupadi bemoaned the death of her sons. Overcome with anguish, a furious Draupadi warned the Pandavas, "If you do not kill Ashwatthama, I will kill myself."

Ashwatthama was blessed with immortality. In spite of knowing this fact, Shri Krishna and the Pandavas waged a war against him. Ashwatthama used the *Brahmashirastra* to kill Abhimanyu's son who was still in Uttara's womb. But Shri Krishna saved the life of Uttara's son by standing between the *Brahmashirastra* and Uttara.

Ashwatthama accepted his defeat and as a token of his submission, he pulled out the precious stone which was studded in his forehead and gave it to Bheema. He then left Kurukshetra and went into the forest. For thousands of years, he wandered the forests in a wretched condition. Bheema gifted the precious stone to Draupadi who then got it fixed in Yudhishthira's crown.

48. THE PANDAVAS RETURN TO HASTINAPUR

The war of Mahabharat ended after eighteen days. Shri Krishna and the Pandavas went to Hastinapur. Yudhishthira fell at the feet of Dhritarashtra and Gandhari and sought their forgiveness. Dhritarashtra embraced Yudhishthira and bemoaned the death of his sons. He then called Bheema to him. At that time, Shri Krishna put a giant-sized metal statue in front of Dhritarashtra. Taking the statue to be Bheema, Dhritarashtra embraced it with all his might. The metal statue was broken into pieces! Presuming that he had killed Bheema, Dhritarashtra began to cry. Shri Krishna said to him, "I knew that such a thing would happen. And so, I had put a metal statue in place of Bheema."

Dhritarashtra was relieved to know that Bheema was alive. A weeping Gandhari said to Yudhishthira, "If you had spared even one of our hundred sons, we could have spent the rest of our lives with his support."

However, even Gandhari was aware of the fact that Yudhishthira was not solely responsible for the events that led to the tragic circumstances. It was Duryodhana who had first declared war against the Pandavas.

Gandhari's husband Dhritarashtra was blind from birth. And so, Gandhari always covered her eyes with a piece of cloth. She was burning with rage. She turned her face away because she knew that even a single beam of wrath emitting from her eyes was enough to burn Yudhishthira to ashes. But, in spite of all her precautions, a beam emitting from between her eyes and the cloth, struck Yudhishthira's toe. As a result, the toe got burnt and it became black.

After fourteen long years, the Pandavas met their mother Kunti. They bowed to her and sought her blessings. Meanwhile, Sage Vyasa came to Hastinapur and consoled Dhritarashtra, Gandhari and Vidura. As per Dhritarashtra's wishes, Yudhishthira performed the last rites of all the departed souls of the Kuru dynasty.

He also prayed for the souls to rest in peace. But, when Kunti asked Yudhishthira to perform the last rites of Karna, he was astonished. Kunti then told him the truth about Karna. Yudhishthira was plunged into sorrow. He felt guilty for Karna's death. Yudhishthira thought, "I am a sinner. I committed a grave mistake by having my own brother killed. Karna was the rightful heir to the throne of Hastinapur."

With a big heart, Dhritarashtra and Gandhari forgave the Pandavas. After the period of mourning was over, Acharya Dhaumya performed the coronation ceremony of Yudhishthira. Shri Krishna advised Yudhishthira to go and meet Bhishma for the last time. Bhishma guided Yudhishthira about the duties and responsibilities of a king. He said, "Yudhishthira! Never mourn the death of great men. It is not how long we live but, how well we live that is the most important thing. Always carry out your duties sincerely and follow the path of *dharma*."

Bhishma *pitamaha's* wise words comforted Yudhishthira. Bhishma breathed his last on the day the sun entered the Tropic of Cancer.

Yudhishthira made Bheema the crown prince and appointed Arjuna the Commander-in-Chief of the army. On an auspicious day, they performed the *Ashwamedha yagya*. Yudhishthira earned a good name and was respected as the best king. He won the love and affection of not only his subjects but also all the other kings. King Virata's daughter and Abhimanyu's wife Uttara gave birth to a son who was named 'Parikshit'.

Dhritarashtra, Gandhari and Kunti lived happily with the Pandavas for fifteen years. It was then that Dhritarashtra and Gandhari decided to go and live in a forest. Kunti was also ready to join them. With a heavy heart, Yudhishthira bid them farewell. The three elders of the family spent three years in the forest. They spent their lives fasting and worshipping the Lord. One day, a terrible fire broke out in their *ashram*. Dhritarashtra, Gandhari and Kunti lost their lives in that fire.

49. SHRI KRISHNA'S FINAL FAREWELL

After the Kurukshetra war, Shri Krishna ruled over Dwarika for thirty-six years. The people of Dwarika attained new heights of happiness and prosperity during his rule. Shri Krishna's fame spread far and wide. But immense wealth and riches had made the Yadavas voluptuous, ill-mannered and arrogant.

One day, some sages came to Dwarika. The Yadavas asked a man named Samb to disguise himself as a woman and took him to the sages. They wanted to have some fun and so they asked the sages, "Will this woman give birth to a son or a daughter?"

The sages were enraged with this irresponsible behaviour of the Yadavas. One of them cursed the Yadavas, "This woman will give birth to a mace which will totally destroy the Yadava dynasty."

The Yadavas were terrified to hear the curse of the sage. The following day, Samb gave birth to a mace. The Yadavas broke the mace into pieces and threw them into the sea.

The Yadavas soon forgot everything about the sage's curse. But a strange prickly plant grew out of the broken pieces of the mace which had been thrown into the sea. The leaves of this plant were as sharp as a sword. One day, the Yadavas went to the sea shore for a picnic. They had a hearty meal and enjoyed themselves thoroughly. After drinking heavily, the Yadavas, including Kritvarma and Satyaki, went out of their minds. They not only fought with one another but also hurled verbal abuses at one another. As the fight worsened, the Yadavas uprooted the plants that had grown on the sea shore and started hitting one another with them. Satyaki killed Kritvarma, as a result of which Kritvarma's angry supporters attacked Satyaki. Shri Krishna's son Pradyumna tried to save Satyaki's life. But ultimately, both Satyaki and Pradyumna were killed. All the Yadavas from Dwarika joined this internal strife and at last, none survived. Balarama was so grief-stricken to see the destruction of the Yadavas that he left for Prabhasatirth. He sat in deep meditation and became one with the Supreme Being.

When Shri Krishna came to know that Balarama was no more, he knew that it was time for him to depart from the earth. Hence, he went into a forest and lay himself down under a *peepul* tree. The work which was to be done by him in this incarnation was now accomplished. He now wished to renounce the world through *yoganidra* (a state of half contemplation and half sleep). Meanwhile, a hunter named Jara unintentionally shot an arrow which pierced Shri Krishna's leg. Shri Krishna departed from the earth. Hearing the news of Shri Krishna's death, his father Vasudeva, too, departed from the earth. Later, the waters of the sea flooded Dwarika, destroying it totally.

50. YUDHISHTHIRA GOES TO HEAVEN

The Pandavas were plunged into gloom by the news of Shri Krishna's death. They now wished to renounce the world. So they made up their mind to go on a pilgrimage and then, after scaling the Himalayas, they would go into heaven. The Pandavas, therefore, crowned Abhimanyu's son Parikshit the King of Hastinapur and left for the Himalayas.

Somewhere along the way, a dog started following them. The Pandavas took him along with them to all the places of pilgrimage and finally, to the Himalayas. As they walked on the snow-capped mountains of the Himalayas, Draupadi was the first one to drop down and die. The Pandavas were shocked at her death. But, they left her there and continued their journey. Later, Nakula and Sahadeva died. After some time, Arjuna and Bheema also died in the Himalayas. In spite of being all alone, Yudhishthira continued his journey ahead. The dog was still following him.

As Yudhishthira went a little further, Lord Indra came with his chariot to receive him. Lord Indra asked Yudhishthira to sit in his chariot. Yudhishthira picked up the dog in his arms and sat in the chariot. Lord Indra said, "This dog cannot accompany you. There is no place for a dog in heaven."

Yudhishthira said, "If there is no place for the dog in heaven, I, too, have no desire to go to heaven."

Having said this, Yudhishthira got down from Lord Indra's chariot and added, "This mute animal has been my constant companion. He has always remained faithful to me. He has never deserted me and so I refuse to leave him alone here."

Before Yudhishthira could complete his words, the dog disappeared and there stood before him Dharmaraja. Dharmaraja had assumed the form of a dog in order to test Yudhishthira. He was pleased to hear Yudhishthira's reply.

Yudhishthira went to heaven with Dharmaraja and Lord Indra. He was surprised to see Duryodhana sitting on a grand throne in heaven. Yudhishthira asked one of the angels, "Where is my mother Kunti, my brothers, Draupadi and others? Are they all not in heaven?"

The angel informed Yudhishthira that they were all in hell.

Yudhishthira said to the angel, "In that case, I, too, would like to go to hell. I cannot live without them."

The angel led Yudhishthira on the road to hell. As he was walking down that road, Yudhishthira saw many horrifying scenes. He was fed up with the pathetic scenes and the unbearable scorching heat of hell. He asked the angel, "How long do we still have to go?"

"If you do not wish to go any further, let us return to heaven from here," said the angel.

Suddenly they heard painful cries. The voices were pleading with Yudhishthira to stop there. Yudhishthira asked them, "Who are you? Why are you calling me?"

Yudhishthira got the following replies :

"I am Karna."

"I am Arjuna."

"And I am Bheema...."

In this way, Yudhishthira heard the voices of Nakula, Sahadeva, Draupadi and her sons, Abhimanyu, Kunti and many other near and dear ones. With a heavy heart, Yudhishthira said to the angel, "I love my mother and my brothers. Therefore, I have decided to stay with them."

Braving the unbearable tortures, Yudhishthira spent a thirtieth part of a day in hell. Later Lord Indra and Dharmaraja came to Yudhishthira and said, "We were only testing you. We are happy that you have successfully passed all our tests. You are, indeed, a noble and pious soul. You had to spent a thirtieth part of a day in hell because, just once in your life, you had told a lie. That one lie of yours had killed Drona. Since you are pure now, you can live in heaven. Your mother, brothers and all your near and dear ones are in heaven and are awaiting your arrival there."

Thus, Yudhishthira got his place in heaven along with his mother Kunti, wife Draupadi and his brothers. They enjoyed eternal peace and happiness there.

॥ इति श्री महाभारत कथा संपूर्णा ॥

INTRODUCTION TO THE MAIN CHARACTERS

Shiva : Lord Shankara, Parvati's husband, father of Lord Ganesha and Kartikeya

Parvati : Himalaya's daughter, Lord Shiva's wife, mother of Lord Ganesha and Kartikeya

Shantanu : King of Hastinapur, husband of Ganga (a goddess of heaven) and Satyawati (a fisherman's daughter), father of Devavrata (Ganga's son) and Vichitravirya and Chitrangad (sons of Satyawati)

Chitrangad : Son of Shantanu and Satyawati, Vichitravirya's brother

Daashraja : Satyawati's father, Shantanu's father-in-law

Ganga : A goddess of heaven, Shantanu's wife. She became the mother of the eight gods – the *Ashta Vasus* who were cursed by Sage Vasishtha. As soon as they were born on the earth, she threw seven of them into the waters of the river Ganga so that they could return to heaven. At Shantanu's behest, she kept Prabhasa, the eighth *Vasu*, on the earth.

Vasishtha : A sage who cursed the *Ashta Vasus* to be born as human beings on the earth for stealing his cow Nandini.

Bhishma (Devavrata, Prabhasa) : The eighth *Vasu* who was born as the eighth son of Shantanu and Ganga. Hence, he was also known as 'Gangeya'. He vowed to live as a celibate so that his father could marry Satyawati. Hence, he was called Bhishma.

Satyawati : Daashraja's (chief of fishermen) daughter, Shantanu's second wife, mother of Vichitravirya and Chitrangad. The fragrance of her body spread for miles together and so she was also known as 'Yojangandha'. As a result of her relationship with Sage Parashara, she became the unwed mother of Sage Vyasa.

Vichitravirya : King of Hastinapur, son of Shantanu and Satyawati

Amba : Daughter of the King of Kashi. In her second birth, She was born as King Drupada's daughter. She performed harsh penance to transform herself into a man called Shikhandi.

Ambika : Daughter of the King of Kashi, Vichitravirya's wife, Dhritarashtra's mother

Ambalika : Daughter of the King of Kashi, Vichitravirya's wife, Pandu's mother

Shalva : King of Saubal. He wished to marry Amba (daughter of the King of Kashi).

Prishata : King Drupada's father

Drupada : King of Panchal, father of Draupadi (Krishna, Panchali) and Dhrishtadyumna

Vidura : Son of Ambika's maid, brother of Dhritarashtra and Pandu, Chief Minister of Hastinapur

Shakuni : King Subala's son, Gandhari's brother, maternal uncle of the Kauravas

Subala : King of Gandhar, father of Gandhari and Shakuni

Dhritarashtra : The blind son of Vichitravirya and Ambika, Gandhari's husband, father of the Kauravas, Yuyutsu and Dusshala

Gandhari : Princess of Gandhar, Dhritarashtra's wife, mother of the Kauravas

Pandu : Son of Vichitravirya and Ambalika, father of the Pandavas, husband of Kunti and Madri

Kunti (Pritha) : Daughter of King Shoorsena. She was adopted by King Kuntibhoja and hence, she was called Kunti. Mother of Yudhishthira, Bheema, Arjuna. When Madri immolated herself in the funeral pyre of Pandu, Kunti looked after her sons Nakula and Sahadeva. Surya, the Sun-god had blessed her with a son – Karna, whom she abandoned as soon as he was born.

Adhiratha : Karna's foster father

Vrishasena : Karna's son

Shoorsena : A king of the Yadava dynasty, Kunti's father

Vasudeva : Son of Shoorsena, Kunti's brother, Devaki's husband, maternal uncle of the Pandavas, father of Shri Krishna

Kuntibhoja : Kunti's foster father

Durvasa : A sage who blessed Kunti with a divine *mantra* to invoke any god, who would then appear before her and bless her with a son just like him.

Agastya : A sage, Lopamudra's husband

Sharadwana : A sage

Rushyashringa : A sage

Mahamuni Vyasa : Son of Satyawati and Sage Parashara. He wrote the Mahabharata.

Karna (Vasusena) : King of Anga, Surya–the Sun-god had blessed Kunti with Karna. Since Kunti became the unwed mother of Karna, she placed him in a wooden basket and set it afloat in a river. This basket reached Adhiratha, a charioteer. Karna was brought up by Adhiratha and his wife Radha. He learnt archery from Parashurama.

Madri : Daughter of the King of Madra, Shalya's sister, Pandu's second wife, mother of Nakula and Sahadeva. She immolated herself in the funeral pyre of Pandu.

Parashavi : Vidura's wife, daughter of King Devaka

Yuyutsu : Dhritarashtra's son, stepbrother of the Kauravas, he loved the Pandavas.

Dusshala : Daughter of Dhritarashtra and Gandhari, Duryodhana's sister, wife of King Jayadratha of Sindhu

Jayadratha : King of Sindhu, Dusshala's husband, brother-in-law of the Kauravas. He was killed by Arjuna in the war of Mahabharata.

Duryodhana : Eldest son of Dhritarashtra and Gandhari, Dusshala's brother, Shakuni's nephew, cousin of the Pandavas.

Purochana : Duryodhana's minister

Brihadbala : A king, an ally of Duryodhana

Lakshmana : Duryodhana's son

Satyashrava : A king, an ally of Duryodhana

Dama : A sage. Pandu killed him unknowingly and so he cursed him.

Yudhishthira : The eldest son of Pandu and Kunti. Since Yudhishthira was born by invoking Dharmaraja, he was also known as 'Dharmaraja'.

Bheema : Son of Pandu and Kunti, he was born by invoking Vaayu, the Wind-god. Because of his insatiable hunger, he was also known as 'Vrukodara'. Hidimba's husband, Ghatotkacha's father.

Arjuna (Parth, Kaunteya) : Son of Pandu and Kunti, he was born by invoking Lord Indra. Since he could shoot arrows with both hands, he was also known as 'Savyasachi'. Husband of Ulupi (son–Iravana), Chitrangada (son–Babhruvahana), Subhadra (son–Abhimanyu). His bow was the *gandeev*.

Brihannala : A name assumed by Arjuna during his life incognito

Nakula : Son of Pandu and Madri, Shalya's nephew

Sahadeva : Son of Pandu and Madri, Shalya's nephew, an astrologer, but he never predicted anything unless he was asked.

Dronacharya : Son of Sage Bharadwaja, Kripi's (Kripacharya's sister) husband, Ashwatthama's father, *guru* of the Kauravas and the Pandavas. As a commander of the Kaurava army, he formed the *Chakravyuha*. He was killed by Dhrishtadyumna.

Kripi : Dronacharya's wife, Ashwatthama's mother

Bharadwaja : A sage, Dronacharya's father. King Prishata (King Drupada's father) was his friend.

Kripacharya : *Guru* of the Kauravas and the Pandavas, brother of Kripi (Dronacharya's wife), Ashwatthama's maternal uncle

Parashurama : A sage who taught archery to only Brahmins. Karna had disguised himself as a Brahmin to learn archery from him.

Ashwatthama : Son of Dronacharya and Kripi, Kripacharya's nephew. He was blessed with immortality. A precious stone was studded in his forehead. During the war of Mahabharata, he brutally killed Dhrishtadyumna and five sons of the Pandavas.

Ekalavya : Son of King Hiranyadhenuka of Nishad. When Dronacharya refused to teach him archery, he learnt it on his own. During the war of Mahabharata, he sided with the Kauravas.

Indra : King of gods. Arjuna was born by invoking Indra. Indra disguised himself as a Brahmin, went to Karna and asked him for his *kavacha* and *kundals* in order to protect Arjuna.

Ashta Vasus : The eight gods : Dhara, Dhruva, Soma, Aha, Anil, Anal, Pratyusha, Prabhasa

Draupadi (Krishna, Panchali) : Daughter of King Drupada of Panchal, sister of Dhrishtadyumna and Shikhandi, wife of the Pandavas.

Sairandhri : A name assumed by Draupadi during her life incognito

Dhrishtadyumna : Son of King Drupada of Panchal, brother of Draupadi and Shikhandi. As a commander of the Pandava army, he killed Dronacharya.

Hidimb : A demon who was killed by Bheema, Hidimba's brother

Hidimba : Hidimb's sister, Bheema's wife, Ghatotkacha's mother

Ghatotkacha : Son of Bheema and Hidimba. During the war of Mahabharata, he was killed by Karna.

Bakasura : A demon who harassed the people of Ekachakra. He was killed by Bheema.

Dhaumya : Royal priest of the Pandavas

Shri Krishna (Govind) : Son of Vasudeva and Devaki. Since Kansa wanted to kill him, he was brought up by Nanda and Yashoda in Gokul. He was the King of Dwarika, brother of Balarama and Subhadra, father of Pradyumna and Samb. He was an incarnation of Lord Narayana.

Keshava : The one with curly long hair, Krishna

Samb : Son of Shri Krishna

Balarama : Shri Krishna's brother, Vatsala's father, expert in duel, Duryodhana was his favourite student

Yadavas : The Kshatriyas of the Yadava dynasty

Ulupi : Daughter of King Kairavya, Arjuna's wife, Iravana's mother

Iravana : Son of Arjuna and Ulupi

Chitrangada : Daughter of King Chitravahana of Manipur, Arjuna's wife, mother of Babhruvahana

Babhruvahana : Son of Arjuna and Chitrangada

Subhadra : Shri Krishna's sister, Arjuna's wife, Abhimanyu's mother

Abhimanyu : Son of Arjuna and Subhadra. During the war of Mahabharata, he broke through the *Chakravyuha* formed by Dronacharya and was killed. He had two wives—Vatsala (Balarama's daughter) and Uttara (King Virata's daughter, mother of Parikshit).

Takshaka : King of serpents, Lord Indra's friend. He lived in the Khandavavana.

Kairavya : Ulupi's father

Vasuki : King of the *Nagaloka*

Maya : A demon who lived in the Khandavavana, an expert architect. During the burning of the Khandavavana, Arjuna had saved his life, and in return, he built a magnificent palace for the Pandavas.

Jarasandha : King of Magadha, son of King Bruhadratha. His two queens gave birth to sons, each with half the body. A demoness named Jara's touch joined the two halves together and the baby came to be known as Jarasandha. He attacked Mathura seventeen times. He was killed by Bheema.

Bruhadratha : King of Magadha, Jarasandha's father

Shishupala : Son of King Damaghosh and Shritashrava (Shri Krishna's paternal aunt), King of Chedi, Dhrishtaketu's father. He wanted to marry Rukmini, but she eloped with Shri Krishna. Shri Krishna killed him during the *Rajasuya yagya*.

Dhrishtaketu : Son of Shishupala. He was crowned after the death of Shishupala. His sister Renumati was married to Nakula. He sided with the Pandavas during the war of Mahabharata.

Vikarna : Son of Dhritarashtra and Gandhari, a just man. He protested when Draupadi was brought in the assembly. Bheema was pained to kill him during the war of Mahabharata.

Dusshasana : Son of Dhritarashtra and Gandhari, Duryodhana's brother. He insulted Draupadi in the assembly. During the war of Mahabharata, Bheema killed him and drank his blood.

Narada : Lord Brahma's tenth adopted son, a celibate, attained the title of 'Devarshi'. He could travel all over the Universe with the power of his will.

Maatali : Lord Indra's charioteer

Gandharvas : The Gods of music and dance

Chitrangad (gandharva) : A *gandharva* who killed Prince Chitrangad

Chitrasena : King of the *gandharvas*

Urvashi : An *apsara* of heaven who taught the art of dancing to Arjuna. When Arjuna rejected her love for him, she cursed him.

Varga : An *apsara* of heaven

Lomash : A sage who met Arjuna in the kingdom of Lord Indra. He visited the Kamyakavana to give Yudhishthira the news of Arjuna's well-being and took the Pandavas on a pilgrimage.

Yaksha : A demi-god, Kubera's servant

Virata : King of Matsya, Sudeshna's husband, father of Uttar, Shwet and Uttara. The Pandavas lived in his kingdom during their life incognito.

Shwet : Son of King Virata and Sudeshna, brother of Uttar and Uttara

Sudeshna : King Virata's wife, Keechaka's sister, mother of Uttar, Shwet and Uttara

Keechaka : Brother of Queen Sudeshna (King Virata's wife), A brave commander of the army of King Virata. Bheema killed him because he was harassing Draupadi (Sairandhri) during her life incognito.

Uttar : Son of King Virata and Sudeshna, brother of Shwet and Uttara

Susharma : King of Trigarta. During the battle against King Virat, he was captured by King Virata. During the war of Mahabaharta, he sided with the Kauravas and challenged Arjuna. Arjuna killed him.

Shalya : Son of the King of Madra, Madri's brother, maternal uncle of Nakula and Sahadeva. During the war of Mahabharata, he was forced to side with the Kauravas. He was killed by Yudhishthira.

Sanjaya : Dhritarashtra's charioteer, an honest and just man who often worked as Dhritarashtra's ambassador. Sage Vyasa gifted him with the divine vision so that he could describe war of Mahabharata to Dhritarashtra.

Satyaki : A Yadava, Shri Krishna's trusted friend

Uttara : Daughter of King Virata and Sudeshna, sister of Shwet and Uttar, Abhimanyu's wife, mother of Parikshit

Pradyumna : Son of Shri Krishna and Rukmini, Aniruddha's father. He learnt archery from Arjuna. He was killed during the internal fight between the Yadavas at Prabhasatirth.

Yama : The God of Death

Varuna : The God of Water

Vaayu : The Wind-god

Hanuman : Son of Vaayu, hence, Bheema's brother. He was Sugreeva's minister and a devotee of Lord Rama.

APPENDIX I : GLOSSARY

Aagneyastra : A weapon of the God of Fire

Agni : The God of Fire

Agrapooja : A ceremony to worship the guest of honour first

Amogha Shakti : Lord Indra's weapon

Apsara : A heavenly nymph who entertains the gods in heaven with songs, dance and music

Aryaka : Kunti's maternal grandfather

Ashtavakra : A sage with eight crooked parts of the body

Ashvinikumars : Gods who were experts in the medical science

Astra : weapon

Avisthala : A village near Hastinapur

Brahmashirastra : The most powerful divine weapon the use of which was taught to Arjuna by Dronacharya

Chakravyuha : The circular formation of the army which Drona arranged during his commandership

Devadatta : Arjuna's conch, gifted to him by Maya

Dhananjay : Arjuna

Dwaitavana : A forest where the Pandavas lived during their exile

Ganas : A retinue of Lord Shiva's servants

Gandeev : Arjuna's bow, gifted to him by Agnideva

Gandhamadana : A mountain in the Himalayas

Gurudakshina : fees paid to the *guru*

Hastinapur : Capital city of the Kuru dynasty

Indrakeel : A peak in the Himalayas

Indraprastha : Capital city of the Pandavas

Kamyakavana : A forest on the banks of the river Saraswati. The Pandavas lived there during the early days of their exile

kavacha : armour

kundals : ear-rings

Madra : Kingdom of Madri's father

Mahakarshan astra : A divine weapon

Makandi : A village near Hastinapur

Matsya : Kingdom of King Virata

Nagaloka : The kingdom of snakes

Nandi : Lord Shiva's bull

Nandighosh : Arjuna's chariot, gifted to him by Agnideva

Nandini : Sage Vasishtha's cow, Kamadhenu's calf

Narayanastra : Lord Vishnu's weapon

Panchajanya : Shri Krishna's conch

Parnakuti : A cottage made of branches and leaves

Pashupatastra : Lord Shiva's weapon

Pratismriti : A master of the knowledge of *Pratismriti* could travel at the speed of thoughts.

Rajsuya yagya : A *yagya* performed by a king in order to establish his supremacy

Raudra : Balarama's bow

Sammohan astra : A divine weapon used to make the enemy unconscious

Savyasachi : One who can shoot arrows with both hands, Arjuna

Shami : A tree, abode of the God of Fire

Shatashringa : A mountain

Sudarshanchakra : Shri Krishna's weapon, gifted to him by Agnideva

Swayamwara : A ceremony which allows a princess to choose her husband

Tantripala : A name assumed by Sahadeva during his life incognito

Vajra : Lord Indra's favourite weapon

Varanavata : A village near Hastinapur

Varunastra : Lord Varuna's weapon

Vrikasthala : A village near Hastinapur

Vrukodara : The one with a large appetite, Bheema

APPENDIX II : SHLOKAS

Shri Krishna said :

मात्रास्पर्शास्तु कौन्तेय शीतोष्णसुखदुःखदाः ।
आगमापायिनोऽनित्यास्तांस्तितिक्षस्व भारत ॥ २-१४ ॥

O Arjuna (son of Kunti)! The relation between the senses and the objects (experiences) is like heat and cold, which affect the body; pleasure and pain, which affect the mind. These are but passing clouds and they do not last for ever. O Bharat (Arjuna)! Bear with them.

नैनं छिन्दन्ति शस्त्राणि नैनं दहति पावकः ।
न चैनं क्लेदयन्त्यापो न शोषयति मारुतः ॥ २-२३ ॥

Weapons cannot hurt the soul; fire cannot burn it; water cannot wet it and wind cannot dry it.

सुखदुःखे समे कृत्वा लाभालाभौ जयाजयौ ।
ततो युद्धाय युज्यस्व नैवं पापमवाप्स्यसि ॥ २-३८ ॥

Treat pleasure and pain alike; gain and loss alike; victory and defeat alike. Get ready to fight the war. Thus, you will not incur the sin (of killing someone).

कर्मण्येवाधिकारस्ते मा फलेषु कदाचन ।
मा कर्मफलहेतुर्भूर्मा ते संगोऽस्त्वकर्मणि ॥ २-४७ ॥

Your right is only to work. You have no right on the fruits of the work. Do not hope for the fruits of the work. But, this should not mean that you become inactive or lose interest (enthusiasm) in the work.

यदा यदा हि धर्मस्य ग्लानिर्भवति भारत ।
अभ्युत्थानमधर्मस्य तदात्मानं सृजाम्यहम् ॥ ४-७ ॥

O Bharat! Whenever there is a dearth of righteousness in the world and there is a danger of lawlessness becoming prevalent in the world, I incarnate myself : I appear.

ब्रह्मार्पणं ब्रह्म हविर्ब्रह्माग्नौ ब्रह्मणा हुतम् ।
ब्रह्मैव तेन गन्तव्यं ब्रह्म कर्म समाधिना ॥ ४-२४ ॥

Whatever is dedicated to Brahma (the Supreme), (that action) is Brahma. All the material that is offered into the *yagya* (sacrificial fire) is Brahma. The *yagya* is Brahma; the host is Brahma; his action (of offering oblations into the *yagya*) is Brahma. Thus, the one who seeks Brahma in all the matters related to the work will (due to the results of his work) realize the Supreme.

निर्मानमोहा जितसंगदोषा अध्यात्मनित्या विनिवृत्तकामाः ।
द्वन्द्वैर्विमुक्ताः सुखदुःखसंज्ञैर्गच्छन्त्यमूढाः पदमव्ययं तत् ॥ १५-५ ॥

The one who is free from attachments and has no feeling of "I"; the one who is steady and zealous; whose mind is unattached everywhere; who has subdued himself and has no desires; the one who has treated pleasure and pain alike; the one who has sought the Supreme; such righteous man is worthy of becoming one with the Supreme.

———————

by
Kumar Jaimini Shastri
Smt. U. J. Shastri

RAMAYANA
THE EPIC
(For Children)

English Adaptation
Asmita Bhatt

In this age of communications revolution, we rarely find time to talk to our children. Today, children are brought up in nuclear families where, usually, both parents are working parents. They do not find much time to spend with their children. Gone are the days when parents or grandparents used to tell the stories from the *Ramayana* to children at bedtime.

But how can we deprive our children of this rich heritage? Keeping this in mind, we are glad to publish the *Ramayana* for children.

The original *Ramayana* is a wonderful epic with many heroic characters, dramatic incidents and popular legends. We have attempted to judiciously select the characters and incidents so as to make the reading interesting and understandable. Written in simple and lucid language, this narrative is a summary of the great epic.

We hope this book will encourage children to gain knowledge and inspire them to build a strong moral fibre. The beautiful pictures on every page will appeal to children and inspire them to take interest in the art.

navNeet ®

THE IMMORTAL CHARACTERS

OF

THE RAMAYANA
(For Children)

by
Yogesh Joshi

English Adaptation
Asmita Bhatt

A set of four books to acquaint children with the immortal characters of the *Ramayana*.

BOOK 1 : 1. SHRAVANA – 1   2. SHRAVANA – 2   3. LITTLE RAMA
          4. PRINCE RAMA   5. KAIKEYI – 1   6. KAIKEYI – 2

BOOK 2 : 7. BHARATA – 1   8. BHARATA – 2   9. SITA
          10. SITA'S ABDUCTION   11. JATAYU

BOOK 3 : 12. SHABARI   13. VAALI   14. HANUMANA
          15. HANUMANA IN SEARCH OF SITA
          16. HANUMANA SETS LANKA ON FIRE

BOOK 4 : 17. VIBHEESHANA   18. LAKSHMANA   19. RAVANA
          20. RAMA AND RAVANA ON THE BATTLEFIELD
          21. SITA'S ORDEAL BY FIRE

The books in this set are written in simple and lucid language with a view to capturing the imagination of children. The style, language and attractive pictures in these books will encourage creativity in our young readers and help them develop a deep sense of understanding and reasoning. We hope these books will encourage self-reading in children and inspire them to develop a strong moral mind-set.

Give your children the treasure of 'The Immortal Characters of the *Ramayana*'.

THE IMMORTAL CHARACTERS
OF
THE MAHABHARATA
(For Children)

English Adaptation
Asmita Bhatt

by
Yogesh Joshi

A set of five books to acquaint children with the immortal characters of the *Mahabharata*.

BOOK 1 : 1. BHISHMA 2. BHISHMA'S SOLEMN VOW 3. KARNA – 1
4. KARNA – 2 5. DRONA 6. EKALAVYA

BOOK 2 : 7. MIGHTY BHEEMA 8. BHEEMA SLAYS BAKASURA
9. BHEEMA SLAYS JARASANDHA 10. BHEEMA IN KURUKSHETRA
11. DRAUPADI'S SWAYAMWARA 12. DRAUPADI IS DISHONOURED

BOOK 3 : 13. YUDHISHTHIRA IS INVITED TO A GAME OF DICE
14. YUDHISHTHIRA LOSES THE GAME OF DICE
15. YUDHISHTHIRA TELLS A LIE 16. KRISHNA'S CHILDHOOD
17. SHRI KRISHNA 18. KUNTI

BOOK 4 : 19. ARJUNA'S SINGLE-MINDEDNESS 20. ARJUNA WINS DRAUPADI
21. ARJUNA'S PREPARATIONS FOR THE WAR
22. ARJUNA AS BRIHANNALA 23. ARJUNA IN KURUKSHETRA
24. ABHIMANYU 25. GANDHARI

BOOK 5 : 26. DURYODHANA – 1 27. DURYODHANA – 2 28. ASHWATTHAMA
29. DHRITARASHTRA 30. BHISHMA ON A BED OF ARROWS
31. YUDHISHTHIRA IN HEAVEN

With a view to acquainting children with the immortal characters of the *Mahabharata*, we are glad to publish this set of five books. The style, lucid language and attractive pictures will help children imagine, understand and analyze the circumstances that led to the war of *Mahabharata* and also think judiciously about its consequences. Each incident in this narrative has a hidden message in it – the message of world peace. It teaches the children the significance of deep, clear thinking and right actions.

The teachings of the Gita are included in a simplified form so as to make the reading and comprehension interesting and inspiring.

We hope these books will entertain and educate our young readers. Give your children the treasure of 'The Immortal Characters of the Mahabharata'.

Why Original Stories?

Hundreds of books are published every year for children. But, we don't have good original stories. Most of the children's stories written in India are mythological or historical. For original stories, we still depend on foreign publications. Hence, our maiden attempt to publish original children's stories.

Children's stories cannot be created, they happen. A child's life is full of stories. Each day in a child's life is full of interesting incidents. We have just woven these incidents into words and colourful pictures. These stories are so real, so interesting and so amusing that we are confident children will not put the book aside till they finish it. All the books are adorned with cute colourful pictures.

With a view to being closer to our young readers, we have also released audio cassettes based on these story books. Now, children will have the advantage of listening and reading the stories simultaneously; which is said to be one of the best ways to learn a language.

We dedicate our interesting original books to our young citizens.

Published & Printed by : Navneet Publications (India) Ltd. 02 (2)